In Memory of Wonder's Child
JACK WILLIAMSON

April 29, 1908 – November 10, 2006

All proceeds from the sale of
this book will be donated to the
Jack and Blanche Williamson Scholarship Fund

FIRST EDITION

Photographs courtesy of the Jack Williamson Science Fiction Library at Eastern New Mexico University's Golden Library
Special thanks to Bonnie Dee for proofreading the manuscript
Cover photograph by Betty Williamson

HAFFNER PRESS
5005 Crooks Road Suite 35
Royal Oak, Michigan 48073-1239
www.haffnerpress.com

ISBN-13: 978-1-893887-26-8

Library of Congress Cataloging-in-Publication Number: 2007925975

Printed in the United States of America

In Memory of Wonder's Child

JACK WILLIAMSON

April 29, 1908 – November 10, 2006

Edited by
STEPHEN HAFFNER

HAFFNER
Royal Oak, Michigan
2007

Jack Williamson in his study (2005)

CONTENTS

IN MEMORY OF WONDER'S CHILD

Stephen Haffner

It is impossible to encapsulate the life of Jack Williamson in a book of this size, but with input from attendees of the memorial service for Jack Williamson on November 16th, you hold the final result in your hands. Connie Willis suggested that "Nonstop to Mars" should be included as a representation of Jack's early pulp SF, and I wanted his last published story "The Mists of Time" to close out the book. With few exceptions, most of the tributes from colleagues in the SF world in this book originally appeared in the December 2006 and January 2007 issues of *Locus* magazine. Jack's passing was widely reported in the mainstream media, and Dennis McLellan's obituary from the *L.A. Times* was superior to all others. John Clute's obituary from *The Independent* was the best summation from an insider's point of view. Lacking from this book is an example of Jack's large amount of academic and autobiographical works. Thankfully, an expanded version of *Wonder's Child* was released in 2005.

A small story: Despite almost living to 100, Jack's work in later years was amazingly youth-oriented and optimistic. This youthful outlook was on display for me when I was in Portales gathering more material for *Seventy-Five* in December 2002. At the Williamson Ranch, Betty Williamson posed co-editor Rick Hauptmann, Jack, and I in front of his writing cabin for a photo to be used on the dustjacket. As we take our places in the blinding sun on the uneven ground, Betty says, "Okay, say 'cheese!'" and Rick and I break out our pearly whites, but Jack says: "Cheese, pretty please . . . cheese, pretty please," just like we all did when we were five years old. The juxtaposition of an old man unashamedly acting like a child made me admire Jack even more.

Looking back on that moment now—with my memories of his stories, and cherished moments enjoying his company and that of his family and friends—to me he will be forever wonder's child.

—*Stephen Haffner*

Vol. 1
No. 4

FALL
1928

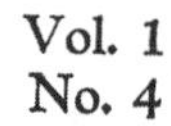

HUGO GERNSBACK, *Editor*
MIRIAM BOURNE, *Asso. Editor* WILBUR C. WHITEHEAD, *Literary Editor*
Dr. T. O'CONOR SLOANE, Ph.D., *Asso. Editor* C. A. BRANDT, *Literary Editor*
Editorial and General Offices: 230 Fifth Avenue, New York, N. Y.

Scientifiction, Searchlight of Science

By Jack Williamson

SCIENCE ever widens our conception of the material universe. We drift farther from the old idea of man as the chief end of creation. To the savage, the universe is his valley, with the heavens arching low overhead, and himself, supreme. Science has found a million new worlds, and lost itself in them. Earth has become a cosmic mote; man, utterly ephemeral and insignificant. *Science* and *Intelligence* alone remain considerable quantities. Then, if the life of the earth is the briefest instant in Time, a question rises: Must man pass with the earth, or will *Human Intelligence* rule on, a new factor in the universe? The idea is stupendous. Science is the doorway to the future; scientifiction, the golden key.

The chief function of scientifiction is the creation of real pictures of new things, new ideas, and new machines. Scientifiction is the product of the human imagination, guided by the suggestion of science. It takes the basis of science, considers all the clues that science has to offer, and then adds a thing that is alien to science—imagination. It goes ahead and lights the way. And when science sees the things made real in the author's mind, it makes them real indeed. It deals only with that which it can see, or weigh, or measure; only with logical hypothesis, experiment and influence and calculation. Scientifiction begins with the ending of science.

The realization of scientifiction is proverbial. Science has made hardly a single step that scientifiction has not foretold. And science, in return, has disclosed a million new and startling facts, to serve as wings for the scientifiction author's brain.

Scientifiction takes a thousand accumulated facts and builds them into a real, impressive picture of ages past, whereby the future of the race may be foretold. It mounts a Time Machine and ventures through futurity, revealing the results of known conditions and tendencies.

Science knows that life on other worlds is possible, but it remains for scientifiction to make the vision real, and to suggest the space flier to verify it. Then science may build the flier, and see for itself. The boundless energy of the atom, the Fourth Dimension, the sub-universe below and the super-universe above, are scientific absurdities all, until scientifiction gives them reality.

And science goes on, with scientifiction as the searchlight. Here is the picture, if we can but see it. A universe ruled by the human mind. A new Golden Age of fair cities, of new laws and new machines, of human capabilities undreamed of, of a civilization that has conquered matter and Nature, distance and time, disease and death. A glorious picture of an empire that lies away past a million flaming suns until it reaches the black infinity of unknown space, and extends beyond. The picture is incredible to us now. Even in the light of scientifiction it is distorted and vague. The idea of the final product of evolution is beyond us. But a sublime picture is that scientifiction may build through the ages, and that science may realize for the ultimate advancement of man.

JACK WILLIAMSON,
Elida, New Mex., East Star R.

$50.00
WILL BE PAID
FOR
EVERY EDITORIAL
PRINTED HERE
See page 670

The Next Issue of the Quarterly Will Be on the Newsstands January 20th

TO JACK WILLIAMSON'S SCIENCE FICTION FAMILY

Betty Williamson

On behalf of Jack's biological family, an enormous heartfelt thank you to the writers, editors, publishers, and fans that enriched his life and allowed him to have an amazing career that spanned nine decades.

I believe I was in my twenties before I came to realize the impact that Uncle Jack had outside of our immediate family and our local community. I attended my first convention with him sometime in 1985 in Baltimore MD. It was Jack's first public appearance since the death of his wife, Blanche, and while the organizers had invited him, they had not expected him to appear. Jack was welcomed with such warmth and love and veneration. I've never forgotten how it felt to walk through the halls of the hotel with him and see the sheer delight on the faces of fans when they spotted him.

Jack told us many times, "I have wonderful friends." Over the years, many of them (or perhaps I should say many of you . . .) have made the trek to Portales and out to the ranch where Jack grew up and where our family still lives today. Jack was right. He *did* have wonderful friends. Many have become special friends of our family. The outpouring of support and tributes we have received since his death has been truly overwhelming.

I hope that you know how much Jack truly loved science fiction, his colleagues, his friends, and all the opportunities that this life and career afforded him. And, yes, I can assure you: he really *was* that nice.

—*Betty Williamson*

JACK WILLIAMSON (1908-2006)
Obituary from *Locus,* December 2006

JACK WILLIAMSON, 98, died peacefully at home on November 10, 2006 in Portales, New Mexico, surrounded by his family.

This legendary SF writer's career spanned nearly 80 years, beginning with stories in the pulp magazines of the '20s and continuing into the 21st century. He published his first story in 1928, and his last stories in 2006, garnering major awards, critical acclaim, and a devoted group of fans along the way. His work as a teacher and proponent of SF's relevance was equally important.

In the contours of his career the entire shape of modern science fiction can be seen.

Williamson began reading SF in 1926 and became a lifelong devotee. His first publication was a guest editorial in *Amazing* in 1928, called "Scientifiction, Searchlight of Science." His first short story, "The Metal Man" (1928), was heavily influenced by A. Merritt. Williamson's first "book" was a pamphlet, *The Girl from Mars* (1929, with Miles J. Breuer), published by Hugo Gernsback to promote *Air Wonder Stories.*

Most of Williamson's early novels were serialized in various magazines, including *Science Wonder Stories, Amazing, Weird Tales,* and *Astounding;* many were later rewritten for book publication.

The Legion of Space (1934, 1947) and its sequels gave us our first major galactic empire, and introduced one of SF's most popular characters, Giles Habibula, based on Shakespeare's Falstaff. *The Legion of Time* (1938, 1952) was one of the earliest significant explorations of large scale time travel.

Williamson's most important early novel is *Darker Than You Think* (1940, 1948), which posits a scientific basis for lycanthropy, is

completely character driven, and explores the scary edge of psychology. *The Humanoids* (1947, 1949) explores notions of artificial intelligence and humanity, still being argued today. His story "With Folded Hands" (1947) began the Humanoids sequence, and is widely considered one of his finest works. His two Seetee books, *Seetee Shock* (1949, 1950) and fix-up *Seetee Ship* (1951) are the earliest works on the then-recently postulated anti-matter. The former also explores terraforming, a term he had earlier invented.

In the 1950s, Williamson's productivity was slowed by writer's block, though he did produce a few novels and several collaborations. With James E. Gunn he wrote *Star Bridge* (1955), and began a long series of collaborations with Frederik Pohl with the *Undersea* Trilogy (1954-58), the *Starchild* trilogy (1963-68), and the Cuckoo series, *Farthest Star* (1975) and *Wall Around a Star* (1983). Other collaborations with Pohl are *Land's End* (1988) and *The Singers of Time* (1991).

Williamson's most important contribution of this period was thriller *Dragon's Island* (1951), which was the first fiction to use the term "genetic engineering" and was one of the earliest SF/thriller novels. It appeared first as an original hardcover from a major publisher—another new beginning for Williamson and for SF. *The Trial of Terra* (1962), a fix-up of 1950s stories, is also significant.

In the late '60s his productivity increased, with new novels including *Bright New Universe* (1967), *The Moon Children* (1971, 1972), and fix-up *Brother to Demons, Brother to Gods* (1979), where the human race is recreated via DNA, clones, and genetic engineering.

Williamson's true renaissance took place in the 1980s, however, with new books that showed all the vigor and curiosity of his best early work, including *Manseed* (1980), *Firechild* (1986), and his Eldren series: *Lifeburst* (1984) and *Mazeway* (1990). He didn't slow down in the '90s, producing *Beachhead* (1992), *Demon Moon* (1994), *The Black Sun* (1997), and a remarkably up-to-date thriller, *The Silicon Dagger* (1999). In the 21st century he published Campbell Memorial Award winner *Terraforming Earth* (2001), which included his 2000 novella "The Ultimate Earth," which won both the Hugo and the Nebula, making him the oldest author to ever win those awards. His last novel was *The Stonehenge Gate* (2005). His later novels no longer had a hero that saved the world/solar system/galaxies. The universe is a much darker place, and so are many of the stories.

Williamson's collections are *The Pandora Effect* (1969), *People Machines* (1971), *The Early Williamson* (1975), *The Best of Jack Williamson* (1978), *Into the Eighth Decade* (1990), and *Dragon's Island and Other Stories* (2002). In the late '90s Haffner Press began an ambitious series to collect all Williamson's short work, producing *The Metal Man and Others, The Collected Stories of Jack Williamson, Volume One* (1999), followed by additional volumes *Wolves of Darkness* (1999), *Wizard's Isle* (2000), *Spider Island* (2001), and *The Crucible of Power* (2006). A vast retrospective, *Seventy-Five: The Diamond Anniversary of a Science Fiction Pioneer,* was published in 2004.

Williamson did some significant non-fiction devoted to SF. His master's thesis was titled *A Study of the Sense of Prophecy in Modern Science Fiction* (1957), and his doctoral dissertation is *H.G. Wells: Critic of Progress* (1966). He won a Pilgrim award in 1973 for his contributions to SF scholarship. For many years he maintained a comprehensive list of all SF-related courses taught in American universities. His Hugo award-winning autobiography *Wonder's Child: My Life in Science Fiction* appeared in 1984. It was updated in 2005.

John Stewart Williamson was born April 29, 1908 in an adobe hut in Bisbee Arizona, when Arizona was still a territory, not a state. When he was six weeks old, his family moved to Mexico, but fled from the revolution there a few years later. He lived in Texas briefly, and in 1915 his family traveled by covered wagon to a homestead in New Mexico, settling in the area where Williamson would live for most of his life. His homestead in Pep, New Mexico is still a working ranch, run by his brother's family. He enrolled in West Texas State University as a chemistry major in 1928, leaving in 1930 to spend a few months in California. In 1931 he took a motorboat trip down the Mississippi with Edmond Hamilton, traveling from Minneapolis to Vicksburg, and continuing by riverboat to New Orleans where they visited E. Hoffmann Price. In 1932 he rode the rails, hopping freight trains and traveling to Denver and back to New Mexico. That fall he enrolled at the University of New Mexico at Albuquerque, but quit school in 1934 to spend several months in Key West, Florida.

In 1936 Williamson began a course of psychoanalysis at the Menninger Clinic in Topeka, Kansas, hoping to overcome persistent psychological and physical problems. He left the clinic in 1937, and traveled to New York, where he met John W. Campbell, Jr. Back in New Mexico he continued writing and made improvements to his cabin at the ranch. On his next trip to New York, in 1939, he met the Futurians, including Frederik Pohl, Donald A. Wollheim, and Cyril Kornbluth. He also met Isaac Asimov (who had sent him several fan letters) and attended the first World Science Fiction Convention. Afterward he lived for a few months in Santa Fe, New Mexico, but in 1940 he returned to California and became friendly with Robert A. Heinlein, regularly attending Heinlein's Mañana Literary Society meetings.

Williamson reported for military service in 1942, serving until 1945 as a weather forecaster in the US and the South Pacific. In 1946 he returned to New Mexico, briefly taking a newspaper job in 1947. He married Blanche Slaten Harp in 1947, becoming stepfather to her two adult children. In 1949 Williamson began building a house in Portales, New Mexico, where he lived for the rest of his life. In 1951 he created comic strip *Beyond Mars,* which was syndicated until its cancellation in 1955. After the strip was canceled he needed a new source of income, so he returned to college at Eastern New Mexico University, earning a Master's in 1957. He taught high school English in Roswell, 90 miles away, which forced him to commute back and forth on weekends. In 1959 he enrolled at the University of Colorado at Boulder—where he also taught as an assistant professor—earning his PhD in 1964, at the age of 58. He became an English professor at Eastern New Mexico University in Portales, where he remained until retirement in 1977; they gave him an honorary doctorate in 1981. The first Williamson Lectureship was held in 1977, a tradition that continued annually for 30 years, with special guests invited to discuss the sciences and humanities. He endowed the Jack Williamson Science Fiction Library at the university in 1982. It contains his books and papers, and has grown into one of the largest science fiction collections in the world. Williamson also endowed the humanities building at the university, which is named after

him. Jia Chuofei, a sculptor from Xian Jiao Tong University in China, donated a large bronze bust of Williamson to Eastern New Mexico University in 2004.

After retirement Williamson traveled the world extensively, continued to write, served as a judge for the Writers of the Future competition, acted as SFWA president from 1977-78, and taught classes in his capacity as Professor Emeritus. He retired from writing after publishing his last novel in 2005 and writing three stories he'd promised to editors.

Williamson is one of the most honored names in SF. He was named a SFWA Grand Master in 1976, only the second person so honored, after Robert A. Heinlein: won a World Fantasy life achievement award in 1994, became an SF Hall of Fame Living Inductee in 1996, won a Stoker life achievement award in 1998, won an L. Ron Hubbard lifetime achievement award in 1998; and became a World Horror Grandmaster in 2004. He was guest of honor at countless conventions, and was the subject of a PBS television special, *Jack Williamson: Wonder's Child* (1995).

In a supplement to his will, written in 1994, Williamson says, "I have had a rewarding life, enjoying many friends, doing work I nearly always loved, and learning all I could about our planet and our fascinating universe. I realize that death is the natural end of life, and I face it with no irrational fear. I expect neither punishment nor reward in any hereafter. My own chief regret is all the writing I can never finish. I am trying to be as ready as I can be for the event when it comes, and I beg my relatives and friends to accept the fact as cheerfully as I hope to."

He willed the copyrights to his published works to Eastern New Mexico University, to fund the Jack Williamson Science Fiction Library and the annual Williamson Lectureship.

Jack Williamson was predeceased by his wife, who died tragically in an auto accident in 1985. He is survived by his brother Jim (who is 95), his niece Betty Williamson Bickley, his nephews Stewart and Gary, and his stepdaughter Adele Lovorn.

In lieu of flowers, the family suggests contributions to the Jack and Blanche Williamson Scholarship, ENMU Foundation, ENMU Station #8, Portales, NM 88130 or to the Portales Public Library, 218 South Avenue B., Portales, NM 88130.

APPRECIATIONS I

JACK
Frederik Pohl

Jack Williamson was a friend, and a very dear one, for most of my life, and, now that I think of it, even for most of his own remarkably long life as well. We first met in 1939. The last time I saw him was in this year of 2006, and that's a stretch of 67 years. Not many friendships survive that long, but then there aren't many people Iike Jack around. I am astonished to realize that, in 67 years, I don't remember ever hearing Jack mention a person he couldn't stand, and I certainly never heard any other person announce that he disliked Jack.

The occasion for that 1939 meeting was the first science fiction Worldcon ever, put on in New York City by local SF fans that summer in an attempt to hitchhike on the drawing power of the city's 1939 World's Fair. "World" was a bit of a misnomer for the con, since the home base of everyone in attendance was somewhere in North America. Still a couple of dozen science fiction fans, writers, and general hangers-on did make their way to New York for the occasion. Including, from New Mexico, Jack.

I didn't meet him at the con, though. I wasn't there. New York fan clubs were quarrelsome, and the club running the con, the Queens Science Fiction League, chose to expel most of the members of the one I belonged to, the New York Futurians. But in retaliation we announced that we would run our own con the next day, and all of the writers and fans present were invited to come to it. Although it was to be held in far-off Brooklyn, which few out-of-towners are willing to navigate, eight or ten of the fans and one of the writers did show up.

The one writer, of course, was that always venturesome explorer, Jack Williamson.

What Jack made of these surroundings he never told me. I think they may have been something of a shock to him, though, because the only meeting space we had been able to line up on short notice was also the headquarters of the local Communist Party.

I have only the vaguest memory of what we talked about at this meeting. I am sure one subject was the iniquity of the QSFL Worldcon committee in kicking us out. I suspect we also chatted about such usual SF subjects as whether Leo Morey was as good a cover artist as Frank R. Paul, and whether there was any hope that this new kid editing *Astounding,* John Campbell, would be able to keep the quality of the magazine as high as F. Orlin Tremaine, the editor who had preceded him. What I do remember is that it seemed to me we had a pretty good time. When it was over and Jack Williamson and the others had gone their ways, I rather hoped, without much actual expectation, that we would meet again.

Curiously, we did. World War II came along and reshuffled everybody's life and various other events took place, and in the summer of 1943 I wound up in the Air Force's weather school, in Chanute Field, Illinois. So, coincidentally, did Jack. He was already a veteran of almost a year in the field as a weather observer and now he was back at Chanute to get some advanced training in weather forecasting. Spending a little GI time with Jack was a totally unexpected pleasure, but it didn't last. The Air Force's training cycles moved along pretty briskly. In just a few weeks Jack was off to (ultimately) the little island in the Pacific where he finished out the war and I, after several stops along the way, to a B-24 bomb group in Italy.

But the war didn't last forever, either. (It just felt that way.) Come peace, and both Jack and I headed back to the civilian world of science fiction. I found myself trying to help a friend, Dirk Wylie, start a literary agency because the hurts he had taken in his time in the Battle of the Bulge had made him unable to do anything more physically demanding; then, when Dirk's health deteriorated even further, I turned out to be running the agency, with Jack Williamson as one of my favorite clients.

The period that followed World War II was a golden dawn for science fiction writers. The big book publishers, led by Doubleday and Simon & Schuster, had just discovered that there was a market out there that was hungry for science fiction novels, and the publishers were falling over each other trying to sign up SF's top writers. Jack Williamson, of course, was high on almost everyone's

wish list. The dark side of this bright age was that there were more offers for Williamson novels than there were Williamson novels to sell. When I wrote Jack to urge him to step up production he replied that there was only one of him and he was writing as fast as he could. However, he said, there was one unexploited possibility. Years before he had tried to write a novel about adventures under the sea. It hadn't worked out. He had abandoned the project, but if I wanted to take it over he was willing. What he then sent me was about 150 pages of manuscript, quite a lot of it repeating the same events in two or three different treatments. But I liked what I saw; I took the collaborative task on and when the book was finished it was published as by both of us under the title *Undersea Quest.*

It wasn't just carrying on with our professional careers that kept our friendship going, nor even our shared fondness for science fiction itself. We had another joint interest. We were intrigued by this planet we inhabited, and we liked to go out and look at as much of it as we could.

This, over the years turned out to be quite a lot, from visiting the Chinese panda-breeding station in the foothills of Tibet and sharing a meal of boiled sheep in Inner Mongolia's steppes of central Asia to doing our best to retrace the steps of the narrator around conquered London in H.G. Wells's *The War of the Worlds.* And to visiting the sites of some famous flying saucer to check out just what kind of people were telling this kind of stories. (More often than not, honest but mistaken ones, we judged.) And of course to attending SF cons just about everywhere, in most of the states of the USA and in so many foreign countries that I've lost count.

And now all of that is forever over.

I can't face that fact without a ton of regret, because an occasion for regret is what it is. It's saddening and there's no way around it. . . .

But, on the other hand, even though we don't have Jack to share our lives any more, aren't we all incredibly lucky to have had him with us for so very long?

—*Frederik Pohl*

JACK WILLIAMSON

Robert Silverberg

Two Jack Williamson anecdotes can, I think, serve to define the man:

In 2004 I was in Portales, New Mexico as one of the two Williamson Lecturers for that year. Fred Pohl and I held forth on the subject of space opera. Jack Williamson was just about to turn 96.

Later that day, at a party at Jack's pleasant suburban home, I promised that I would come back to Portales four years hence for his 100th birthday party. He gave me a long, slow look, and then he said, in that high-pitched Southwestern drawl of his, "Well, Bob, you seem to be in pretty good shape. You just might make it."

The next day, as I was about to leave, I went to him to say goodbye. And Jack said to me—I don't think he intended any reference to his joke of the day before—"I wish you a long life, Bob."

The first anecdote reveals that behind the slow, aw-shucks affect of his personal style lay a sly, quick wit not readily apparent to a casual observer. The second story shows that even though he was nearly 96 years old, an age at which many people, bowed down with aches and pains, are quite ready to shuffle along, Jack Williamson still loved life enough to wish me—a mere stripling of 69, at the time—the sort of lengthy one that he had had.

He had a long life, all right, and it was an amazing one. Not that it was entirely a joyful one, as he made quite clear in his unsparing autobiography, *Wonder's Child.* There were plenty of dark moments along the way. But he withstood them all, and he lived on and on into as serene and enviable an old age as I can imagine, still active intellectually and creatively almost to the end, surrounded by a loving and supportive community of friends, and revered by three generations of his colleagues for his tremendous contributions to the field in which he worked.

I thought he'd live forever. Honestly. I never expected to hear the phone call that came yesterday: "Jack Williamson just died." Well,

98-years-plus is no trivial span, and it was time for him to slip away, and away he went. We of the science-fiction world are in a new era, now, because he was on the scene virtually from the beginning—his first story was published just two years after Hugo Gernsback founded *Amazing Stories*—and no one now living has ever experienced a time when Jack Williamson was not a central figure in science fiction. We'll have to get used to that, I guess. But what a privilege it was to have had him among us these many decades. And what a delight it was to have known him.

—*Robert Silverberg*

JACK

Frank Robinson

Jack Williamson published his first short story—in *Amazing*—two years after I was born. The first story of his I read was "Crucible of Power" in the February 1939, issue of *Astounding*—the first science fiction magazine I ever bought (I was 13 years old and ready to graduate from Jules Verne and H.G. Wells).

Two issues later, *Astounding* carried the first installment of "One Against the Legion," his homage to Shakespeare in the character of Giles Habibula, a futuristic Falstaff. His early space opera was some of my favorite reading—he didn't have the galactic scope of E.E. Smith but he had fascinating plots and vivid characterization. If you borrow from Shakespeare, you borrow from the best.

Some years later, I had the pleasure of introducing Jack at a science fiction convention in San Jose and couldn't resist the urge to give him a very personal token of my esteem (and the convention's)—a leather bound copy not of the first magazine he'd ever had a story in but of the first magazine in which I'd read my first Williamson story.

He wrote fantasy as well as science fiction, and in the middle '30s thought of branching out into the weird menace pulps. Sometime after my introduction of him, he asked if I'd sell some old pulps for him and we'd split the profits. What he sent me were a few copies of *Horror Stories* and *Terror Tales* and several of *Doctor Death*. He'd obviously changed his mind about writing for the field—the magazines were unread.

Perhaps Jack's greatest influence on me was when he reinvented himself as Will Stewart—to me, at the time, a "new" and fascinating author. Jack was one or the first to try and succeed at it—Heinlein was always Heinlein, and ditto Asimov, van Vogt and some of the other majors. Few of them strayed far from that particular branch of the field in which they felt most at home. Williamson, probably a little unhappy at being considered an "old-timer," took the gamble. For the field itself, he then became something of a renaissance man. He wrote as Williamson and Will Stewart, wrote a comic strip, juveniles (in collaboration with Fred Pohl), and taught science fiction as a college course.

For those of us who yearned for respectability for the field, it was Williamson who took the first giant steps to earn it.

All writers are mortal, but as some of us aged, it was always comforting to consider that Jack was still alive and kicking in his 70s, his 80s, and well into his 90s.

With Jack's passing, the world has suddenly become a much colder place for the rest of us.

—Frank M. Robinson

JACK WILLIAMSON
Connie Willis

Oh, Jack! I hate this! I hoped the day would never come when I'd be writing one of these, when I had to try to sum up what you've meant to me. And to everybody in science fiction. But the day's here. And even though I can't possibly do justice to the subject, here's my attempt:

It was my extraordinary good fortune to have known and loved Jack for nearly thirty years. I met him at the first science fiction convention I ever went to, and he was unbelievably kind to me (as he was to every aspiring author he met) then and at every subsequent convention. As I got to know him over the years, my respect for him grew greater and greater. Then, after I'd had the privilege of being a guest at the Williamson Lectureship at Eastern New Mexico State University, he and his family welcomed me into their homes and lives, and Jack and I became not only close friends, but family. (It Is my secret belief that Jack's niece Betty Williamson, Patrice Caldwell, and I are actually sisters who were separated at birth.) I can't think of anyone I'd rather be related to than Jack.

Everyone who writes appreciations about Jack for *Locus* will use superlatives that will sound exaggerated but aren't. He was every bit as gracious, deferential, kind, thoughtful, gentlemanly, and caring as everyone says, and his contributions to the field can't be overstated.

He was a pioneer, both in science fiction and in his own life. He was born in Arizona when it was still a territory, traveled to New Mexico in a covered wagon, and grew up on a cattle ranch. And he blazed literary trails in a career which spanned over seventy years. He wrote and published work in nine decades, two centuries, and two millennia, and wrote his last story last year.

His stories and novels were groundbreaking, and many of his works—"Nonstop to Mars," *The Legion of Space,* "With Folded Hands," *Darker Than You Think, The Green Girl, The Humanoids,* the Seetee stories, and his moving autobiography, *Wonder's Child*—are classics. He received every award science fiction had to offer, was honored all over the world, had an asteroid named after him, was the second person ever to be made a Grand Master by SFWA, and has words he invented listed in the Oxford English Dictionary. It's a stunning list of accomplishments, but it doesn't begin to describe the magnitude of his contribution to science fiction.

Which was quite simply that, writing on a battered typewriter with a faded purple ribbon in a shack he built himself out in the middle of a field full of rattlesnakes and the middle of the Great Depression, Jack Williamson invented the future.

He wrote about space travel, asteroid mining, Dyson spheres, cloning, black holes, unmanned probes, Mars exploration, and time travel when nobody had ever heard of them. He wrote about antimatter before it was an accepted scientific theory, was one of the first to see the possible criminal side-effects of organ transplants and the unintended consequences of automation and technology to humans, explored psychology and telepathy and linguistics.

He shaped the direction of science fiction, set its tone, and invented its language. His vision ran so far ahead of everyone else's there weren't any words for what he envisioned, and he had to invent his own, words like "androids" and "genetic engineering" and "psionics" and "terraforming," the vocabulary which every science fiction writer uses every day. And he created a vision not only of the future, but of the part science fiction would play in it. "It goes ahead and lights the way," he wrote in 1928. "And when science sees the things made real in the author's mind, it makes them real indeed."

His work inspired entire generations of science fiction writers and scientists. Carl Sagan considered him one of his most formative influences. Isaac Asimov wrote him a fan letter when he was a kid, and every writer writing today uses ideas first explored by Jack whether they're aware of it or not.

Huge numbers of writers were also influenced by knowing him. He knew everybody in the field, from Edmond Hamilton to Leigh Brackett to Robert A. Heinlein to Edward Bryant to young writers fresh out of Clarion West. He served as president of SFWA twice, and his circle of friends reached all through science fiction—from Frederik Pohl & Betty Anne Hull to Walter Jon Williams, Bob Silverberg & Karen Haber, Jim Frenkel—and all of them and many others made the pilgrimage to Portales: Gay & Joe Haldeman, Michael Swanwick, Michael Cassutt, Nancy Kress, Greg Bear, Sage Walker, George R.R. Martin.

And many—Scott Edelman, Stephen Haffner, Eleanor Wood, Walter Jon Williams, Melinda Snodgrass, Daniel Abraham, Craig Chrissinger, Richard Kaminsky, Charles N. Brown—came year after year, wanting to honor Jack. And to fully appreciate that, you have to understand just how much in the middle of nowhere Portales is. You turn left at Albuquerque, drive till you either fall off the end of the earth or hit Texas. Portales is another hour and a half from there. None of those people would have done it for anybody but Jack.

And then there are his many Portales friends: colleague and co-teacher Patrice Caldwell; Gene Bundy, who runs the Jack Williamson collections at the library; his neighbor Rick Hauptmann; his beloved niece Betty; and all the rest of his loving family. It's tempting to say he was lucky to have had such a loving family and circle of friends, but Jack made his own luck. As the Wizard says to the Tin Woodman, "The size of your heart is judged not by how much you love, but by how much you are loved."

Yet in spite of the beloved and revered position he held in the field and in spite of having every award and accolade possible showered on him, he remained self-deprecating and humble. He never bragged about his accomplishments, always seemed surprised by the honors he got, and constantly tried to improve himself and his writing. He studied plotting, read "how to write" books, and went through therapy. Gardner Dozois tells about catching sight of him at a "What We're Looking for at Our Magazines" panel at a convention, sitting among all the aspiring new writers, and asking, "What are *you* doing here, Jack?"

"Well," Jack said in his Western drawl, "I thought I'd like to find out what kind of stories you were looking for and see if I could write something like that."

That attitude kept him publishing through the pulp years, the Golden Age, and the New Wave, when so many other authors foundered, unable to make the jump to new styles and new subject matter. He introduced psychology and linguistics into his work, learned to use e-mail and the Internet, and kept up with cutting-edge technology. He wrote his final novel, *Stonehenge Gate,* at age 96, and won a Hugo Award 27 years *after* he had become a Grand Master of Science Fiction. As John Clute says, "in his work and his life, he has encompassed the field."

To me, his greatest contribution, as a person and a writer, was his sense of wonder. It's a sense that imbues his work, a feeling of delight and awe toward the universe, an undying curiosity about it and a generous open-mindedness toward all the creatures in it. It's a sense of limitless possibility, of hope, of, as he says in his autobiography, *Wonder's Child,* "strange new worlds, brightly alluring, brimming with puzzle and peril and hope." A sense of faith in the future. That sense of wonder established much of the tone for science fiction (echoed in writers from Heinlein to Bradbury's "A Miracle of Rare Device") and was what drew so many readers to it.

But his sense of wonder didn't arise out of his being innocent or naïve. He called himself a "cautious optimist," and that optimism was grounded in a wry humor and a hardheaded common sense. In 1948, when he read in the paper that aliens had crash-landed in Roswell, only sixty miles away, he and Fred Pohl took off to see for themselves. There were not two people on the planet who wanted aliens to have landed more than they did, but after a five minute inspection of the evidence, Jack (who'd been a meteorologist in the South Pacific during World War II) concluded, "It's a weather balloon." Which I consider the definitive verdict on the whole affair.

He managed to keep his sense of wonder his entire life, in spite of disappointments and disillusionments and losses. He never grew despairing and embittered, like Mark Twain, or stopped writing stories and began writing diatribes, like more authors than I can name. At the end of his long life, he was just as optimistic about and interested in the world as he had been as a young kid. He was still teaching science fiction and writing classes last year. When I saw him for the last time in September, we talked about Harry Potter and the Hubble telescope and the upcoming elections. He told me he loved *Spider-Man* and that he was worried about what would happen to the space station if the shuttle program ended. He was, almost to the very end, still reading, still laughing, and still writing. "I've been elated that writing is still great fun to do," he wrote. "The wonder's still alive, and I rejoice that these words aren't yet actually the end—" He remained Wonder's Child to the very end. And Wonder's Father.

He also kept his humility right up to the very end. He had to be talked into letting his family hold a memorial service. He didn't think enough people would come to make it worthwhile. Oh, please! All weekend I have been on the phone with people determined to move heaven and earth to be there, and Betty has received hundreds of e-mails and calls from writers who know how much they owe to him, from people all over the country and the world wanting to express their condolences and their affection for Jack.

All this makes Jack sound like a saint, and although he was certainly the closest thing to it you can find in science fiction, he was not above acerbic comments (especially about editors who never paid) and dry wit and the occasional flash of wickedness (although someone like Michael Cassutt had to be there to bring that out: "Come on, Jack, let's have another drink." "I just believe I will.") He was very funny and intelligent and delightful to talk to, and I wish he was still here.

It's not that I wish him back the way he was when he died. In the last months of his life, he was just about worn out and was ready to go. Last week, he asked his niece Betty, "Am I dying?"

"I think you might be," she said.

"Good," he said.

And I definitely wouldn't wish him one more day, one more second of illness or infirmity or exhaustion. It's just that I wanted . . . you know that great scene in *Indiana Jones and the Last Crusade* where Indy and his dad, both having drunk the water of immortality, ride off into the sunset? That's what I wanted. I wanted him to live forever.

Which he will—in the field and the works and the words he created, in the generations of students he taught, of writers he encouraged and inspired. He'll live on in all the friends he leaves behind, in the vision and the hope he gave us all. In the future he invented for us.

But it's not enough. And I miss him already. When we held a panel in his honor at the Worldcon in Boston, he sent this message: "I love everybody, and I wish I could be there."

I wish you could, too. More than anything.

I love you, Jack. Rest in peace, dear.

—*Connie Willis*

JACK WILLIAMSON

Charles N. Brown

I don't remember exactly where I met Jack, but looking through my collection of autographed Jack Williamson first editions, the earliest I found signed to me was 1952 in Chicago, so it's at least 54 years ago. I do remember that I thought Jack was remarkably old—over 40! An infinite time in the future for a teenager.

Forty years later, we traveled through China together, and Jack didn't seem nearly as old. True, he was over 80, but hadn't slowed down yet. We were rooming together, and since the Chinese venerate age, I thought we would get the best rooms at the various stops and would be given them first. But Jack never seemed as tired as I felt at the end of the day, and didn't seem interested in taking advantage. I finally convinced him to sit down and, at least *act* tired. It was a fascinating and exciting trip where we were VIP guests of the Chinese government, met the governor of Sichuan, traveled to the Panda reservation near Tibet, were trapped there by a mountain storm that destroyed the road, were rescued by the Chinese Army, and finally returned to civilization in Chengdu. The scariest time for me was not during the storm, or the rescue, but when Jack got sick in southern China with pneumonia-like symptoms. He was seen by a Chinese woman doctor, who looked about 12 years old, and given all sorts of strange medicine to take at various times. As his roommate, I did most of the worrying, but Jack treated it as just another annoyance and came through fine.

I could have lived for years on exaggerated stories from that trip, but Jack went ahead and published an accurate account, limiting me to just facts. Both of us had been to China before, when it was first opened to visitors. My earlier recollections were vague, but Jack, of course, had written his up and could comment on the changes over the decade between trips. He predicted vast changes in the future of China, and he was right.

Jack also watched science fiction change over most of a century, and most important, was able to change with it. No small thing, for a writer or for a human being. We tend to get more settled, more dogmatic in our ways as we get older, clinging to the world we grew up in and knew best.

Not Jack.

Over the past 20 years, I've often made the pilgrimage to Portales, New Mexico for the Williamson Lectureship (and other separate trips). The Lectureship was, of course, the excuse. The real reason was to visit Jack, listen to his sharp, gentle wit, to bask in the light of one of the finest human beings I've ever known.

Jack treated everybody with respect, listened to their lives, their problems, and considered them first as human beings. He was endlessly fascinated (and sometimes appalled) by humanity. He called us all his colleagues. He also treated us as contemporaries. He said, "It isn't the length of time, it's the time we share that makes us contemporaries." I've never forgotten that.

He started writing in that Gernsbackian era of the endless wonderful future, but was not only able to make the changes, but sometimes head us into the glorious galactic empire of *The Legion of Space*—the *Star Wars* of its era—to the complicated time-travel wonders of *The Legion of Time* to the darker visions of the character driven *Darker Than You Think* and the philosophically driven *The Humanoids*.

His books have been on the cutting edge of science as early as in *Seetee Shock* through *Dragon's Island* to the more recent Mars novel *Beachhead* and that SF/fantasy cusp in *Demon Moon*. His final novel, *The Stonehenge Gate,* was written when he was 95.

Thank you, Jack, for the friendship as well as for the wonderful books I've been reading for nearly 60 years. Again, what more can I ask?

—*Charles N. Brown*

Nonstop to Mars

I

SOMETHING WAS QUEERLY wrong—with either the ship or the air. And Carter Leigh knew that it couldn't be the ship. The creaking old *Phoenix* might be obsolescent in a world that the new cathion rockets had conquered, but he knew every bolt and strut of her. Knew her well enough to take her apart and put her up again, in the dark. And loved her, for her loyalty through six years and half a million miles of solo flight.

No, the trouble couldn't be in the *Phoenix*. It had to be the atmosphere.

He couldn't understand it. But the barometric altimeter had kept luring him down, toward frozen peaks that loomed a thousand feet higher than they should have been. The engine labored, and the thrust of it weakened dangerously. And the wind that struck him over the pole was a screaming demon, more freakishly violent than he had ever met before.

It baffled him. Through all the endless, weary night, deaf with the long thunder of the loyal old engine, sitting stiff with cold even in his electrically heated suit, gulping coffee from a vacuum jug, poring over charts and studying instruments with aching bloodshot eyes—ever since the last strange sunset, he had hopelessly picked at the sinister riddle.

Nonstop flights were nothing new to Carter Leigh. Men, looking at the long record of his feats, had nicknamed him "Lucky." But he had something more than luck. In his lean body there was the tremendous endurance that it took to fly on, hour after straining hour, when most men would have dropped over the stick.

And this flight—nonstop from Capetown to Honolulu, across the bottom of the world—had promised to be no harder than the rest. Not until he saw that last sunset.

Behind him, beyond the cragged granite fangs of Enderby Land, as he climbed above the ramparts of the polar plateau, the sunset had been frighteningly strange. An incredible wheel of crimson, rolling along the rim of the world, it had been winged and tufted with eldritch green.

The aurora was another disquieting scrap of the puzzle. It burned above him all that night, whenever the sky was clear, until all the white antarctic wilderness seemed on fire with its sinister and shifting brilliance.

The cold was another thing. Leigh had made polar flights before. But never had he met such merciless temperatures. The motor, even with cowl ventilators closed, grew sluggish with it. It crept into the cockpit and probed deep into his body.

Beyond the pole and Marie Byrd Land, over the dark Antarctic again, he met a wall of cloud. He tried to climb over it. Heavy and dull with altitude and fatigue, he opened the oxygen valve. The vital gas revived him a little. But the plane could not scale the summits of vapor. He flew into them—wondering.

Savage winds battled in the cloud, and it was riven with lightning. Rain hammered the ship, and froze on it, until the ice dragged it almost to the surface. Leigh fought the elements, and fought the mounting weariness in him, and came at last unexpectedly into the calm of a strange northward dawn.

The aurora was fading from a sky grown brilliantly clear. Studded with white points of icebergs, the gray South Pacific was sliding back at three hundred and fifty miles an hour—still a good pace, he thought stubbornly, even if the rockets were three times as fast.

Leigh was peeling an orange, beginning to hope that all the terror of the night had been the child of fancy and fatigue, when he saw the thing in the northeast. Against the red and green of a suddenly disturbing dawn, it fell like a silver thread.

A white, spiral vortex—the funnel of a great tornado. He saw a blob of gray mist about the foot of it, marching over the sea. The upper end of it, oddly, was lost above the bright wings of dawn.

Leigh had never seen a storm just like this one. At first he thought there was no danger to him. But the white, writhing snake of it whipped toward him with an appalling quickness.

It seized the *Phoenix* in a sudden blast of wind, sucking the ship toward that racing funnel. Sea and sky spun madly. He was lifted so swiftly that his eardrums ached. Grimly he fought it, with all his calm skill and all the familiar strength of the ship.

He fought—and won. The white pillar left him fluttering in its wake and marched on into the west. Hurried observation of the higher sun told Leigh that he had been flung fifteen hundred miles northward.

But he knew, with a sinking in his heart, that the *Phoenix* was crippled. Her right aileron had been twisted and jammed by the force of that incredible wind. He would have to set her down.

Whistling the tune of "Barbara Allen," which always seemed to cheer him, Leigh searched the maps. He found a pinprick of land named Manumotu—the only possible haven in a thousand miles—and turned the limping amphibian toward it, flying with rubber and throttle.

One more failure. Two, he reflected bitterly, in a row. For the last flight, two months ago, had failed also, from a cause as strange as that tornado.

A "bipolar" flight, Tick Tinker had called the last one. Tick was the tireless little publicity man, one-legged and one-eyed, who was Leigh's partner in his singular business of wrestling a living from the air. "Bipolar," because the route from Croydon back to Croydon along the prime meridian included both the poles. Leigh had safely rounded the planet, with but three scheduled stops. But the flight had failed just the same, because of the Stellar Shell.

"We're an out-of-doors advertising firm, Lucky," Tick used to say. "You fly for attention value. And I sell it to the makers of oil and piston rings and what-have-you. And it's a legitimate business, so long as you can keep in the headlines."

But all the headlines two months ago had been about the Stellar Shell. Some astronomer named Gayle, the day Leigh took off from Croydon, announced discovery of a mysterious missile plunging out of the depths of space, toward the solar system. The "bipolar" flight had earned no more than a few sticks of space on the inside pages. For the black streamers ran:

STELLAR SHELL SHOT AT PLANETS;
WILL OBJECT STRIKE EARTH?
ASTRONOMERS BAFFLED

When Leigh came in to Croydon again, the flight completed in three grueling days, there was no crowd to meet him. Staggering away from the dusty, oil-spattered *Phoenix,* he himself paused to buy a paper.

COSMIC BULLET HITS MARS;
EARTH SPARED;
NATURE OF OBJECT UNKNOWN

There had been no more news of the Stellar Shell, nothing more than the speculations of bewildered scientists. But the flight was already ruined. Tick Tinker had radiographed:

> CONGRATS ON BIPOLAR FLIGHT. BUT STELLAR SHELL HOGGED THE HEADLINES. FLIGHT TOTAL LOSS FINANCIALLY. YOUR NAME GETTING RAPIDLY UNKNOWN. TESTIMONIALS BEGGING AT CUT RATES. URGENT RELEASE DETAILS NEW PUBLICITY FLIGHT. SUGGEST SOMETHING NONSTOP POLAR. USE ZEROLUBE BRAND OILS FOR TESTIMONIAL.

And so Tick's message had brought him here, dead with fatigue and heading toward a speck of rock that probably had no inhabitant.

The motor covered the windshield with a thin spray of oil, and Leigh stopped his whistling briefly to curse all Zerolube products. He plugged in his helmet phones and switched on the little battery transmitter. It was good for just ten minutes of continuous sending—the *Phoenix* had no room for heavier equipment, not even emergency rations.

"SOS!" he called. "Pilot Leigh in airplane *Phoenix* forced down by storm. Will try to land on Manumotu. SOS—"

The instant reply surprised him:

"Manumotu Station, Gayle Foundation, calling airplane *Phoenix.* Dr. E. K. Gayle speaking. Land on north beach. I will stand by to assist you. Come in, airplane *Phoenix.*"

"Airplane *Phoenix* calling Manumotu Station," gasped Leigh, relieved. "Thanks, Doc. I'll be seeing you, if I can keep out of the water half an hour longer. Signing off."

It took an hour—an hour that seemed endless to Leigh as he fought the fatigue in him and nursed the crippled plane. But at last Manumotu came out of the sparkling northward haze. A cragged volcanic summit appeared sheer on three sides, edged on the north with a scrap of coral beach.

He crossed the beach. A broad rock bench above it was tufted with tropical green. A long shedlike building of white sheet metal stood upon it, a white tent, and a great pile of crates covered with brown tarpaulins. A white flag waved. Then he saw the tiny figure running from the tent toward the beach.

The landing was hazardous. The crippled wing caught the crest of a wave and covered the plane with spray. She staggered, but came up bravely. He taxied in and rolled up on the blinding coral sand.

Following the signals of the flag, he brought the *Phoenix* to a safe dry stop where a rocket must have been moored, for there were deep wheel marks in the sand, and the hibiscus bushes beyond were scorched black as if from rocket jets.

Heavily, his legs as stiff as if they never had been straightened before, he climbed out of the cockpit. The person with the flag came to meet him. A slim young figure, in boots and breeches, khaki shirt open at the throat, yellow head bare. A crisp voice, brisk, impersonal, greeted him:

"Hello. You are the famous Lucky Leigh?"

"In person." He grinned. "And thanks for showing me the way in, doc—"

His jaw fell. This was a woman—a girl. Her intent oval face was dark with sun. Her keen blue eyes were scanning his heavy, swaying body—not altogether, he thought, with approval.

"Oh!" he said. "I thought you were Dr. Gayle."

"I am," she said gravely. "Dr. Elene Kathrine Gayle."

His red eyes blinked at her.

"You—you aren't the Dr. Gayle who discovered the Stellar Shell?"

She nodded.

"My father was a leader in his field of science. He established the Gayle Foundation. But he has been dead five years. I have been trying to carry on his work." She studied him gravely. "Do you object to my discovery?"

"You ruined my last flight," he told her. "I lived through seventy-six hours of hell; I set a record for gasoline flight over both poles. And what with your Stellar Shell, the world never knew I had been off the ground."

"And, I suspect, was little the worse for the fact." Leigh flushed at the hint of sarcasm in her voice. "However—are you hungry?"

"Famished," he told her.

On a rough pine table in the white tent, she slapped down two tin plates, split open cans of meat and butter, indicated a big vacuum urn of coffee, a huge jar of marmalade.

"Proceed," she said.

Leigh's dull eyes were watching her.

"You're the whole crew here?"

Her boyish head nodded.

"Emergency," she said. "The Foundation is establishing twenty new meteorological observatories. Manumotu Station was the most important, because it is directly in the track of the phenomena we are investigating. Therefore, I took charge here myself."

"Alone?"

"I had two assistants. But Dr. French took acute appendicitis, and Cragin flew him out in the rocket. Should have been back yesterday. But didn't show up. I'm carrying on. . . . You said you were hungry."

She dumped half a can of corned beef into her tin plate, passed the remainder to Leigh. But he sat, wonderment rising against his mist of sleep, staring at her.

"Emergency?" he questioned.

She nodded.

"Something is happening to the atmosphere."

"I thought conditions were strange," he said, "flying over the pole."

She pushed back her plate to seize a notebook.

"What phenomena did you observe?" she demanded eagerly.

He told her in a tired sleep-fogged voice about the strangely gaudy sunset, the aurora, the phenomenal cold, the unaccountably low barometric pressures, the singular tornado that had crippled the *Phoenix*.

"What does it all mean?" he concluded. "What is happening?"

"I'm here to find out," she told him. "Sunset and aurora probably due to abnormal electronic bombardment of the ionosphere. But the storms and pressure disturbances are still not accounted for. Unless—"

Her yellow head shook.

"The only conceivable answer is too appalling."

She looked quickly at her wrist watch, dumped the debris from her plate into a pail beside the table, wiped plate and spoon clean with a paper napkin. She rose.

"Excuse me. But the duties of both my assistants have fallen upon me. My time is budgeted. I have forty-eight minutes a day for meals. Now I have instruments to read."

"So that's how a lady astronomer lives." Leigh grinned. "If I can help you—"

She shook her head with evident disapproval.

"I doubt it. Our work here doesn't consist of publicity stunts. . . . Eat as much as you like. You'll find a cot behind the partition. I'll radio directions to your rescue party. Please keep in mind, when you leave, that it is the policy of the Gayle Foundation to avoid unnecessary publicity. Especially, we don't want to alarm the world about these current meteorological phenomena, until we have more comprehensive data."

Leigh was staring at her, a slow anger rising in him. "Look here, you think I'm a pretty bad egg?"

Her keen eyes swept him impersonally.

"Frankly, Mr. Lucky Leigh," her cool voice said, "your existence and your stunts annoy me. I can't see that you serve any creative function. In the precarious early days of gasoline aviation such men as you, testing equipment and exploring routes, may have served a useful end. But now that rockets are as fast and as certain as the sun, you are a mere anachronism."

Leigh opened his mouth to protest. But the girl held up a brown imperative hand.

"I've got no time to listen to you," she said. "Because I have vitally urgent work to do. I am already upsetting my schedule. But I've wanted for a long time to tell you a thing or two."

Her smooth face was flushed a little. He listened to her, grinning.

"Now," she went on swiftly, "if you were trying to fly nonstop to Mars, even if you never got there, that would be a different proposition. Because you would be expanding the horizons of science. You would be doing something different and important.

"But your old gasoline wreck is as far behind the times as you are, Leigh. It is a rocket that will make the first flight to Mars. I know a man who may pilot the first rocket there. He is Laird Cragin—you never heard of him, because he isn't a publicity flier. But he is test pilot for the experimental space rockets that the Foundation has been working on, in association with some Army engineers. You ought to meet him. Because whether he ever gets to Mars or not, he's trying to do something real."

Carter Leigh gulped.

"Listen, Miss Gayle," he protested. "You've got me all wrong. I used to like the glory, I admit. But now it's just a business. I've come to hate the clamor and the crowds, and I always skip the banquets. Tick Tinker is my contact man; he releases the publicity, does the testimonials, handles all the business end. We're just trying to make a living."

Her brown chin squared. And, through the gray haze of fatigue that filled his mind, Leigh suddenly perceived that a lady astronomer could still be very good to look at.

"It is possible," her cool crisp voice was saying, "to make a living in a way that helps others besides yourself. Here you are hopping about the planet, with about as much aim and intelligence as a beheaded flea, while God-knows-what is happening to the very air we breathe!"

She turned decisively away from him.

"You are as extinct as the dodo, Mr. Nonstop Leigh," she told him. "The only difference is that you don't know it. Sleep on that. I've got a barocyclonometer to read."

II

CARTER LEIGH sat over the rough table, staring out of the tent after her hastening boyish figure. He had seen suddenly, behind her brisk impersonal efficiency, that she was very tired—and somewhat frightened.

His brief anger at her frank criticism was all turned back upon himself. After all, it was true that such men as Lindbergh and Byrd and Post and Corrigan hadn't left much to be accomplished in the field of nonstop gasoline flight.

No, he deserved her scorn.

But what had frightened her? What *was* happening to the atmosphere? Leigh's mind grappled for a vain moment with the problem, but he could not concentrate now. All he wanted was a chance to sleep.

He stood up, his body stiff and wooden, and reeled to the cot beyond the canvas partition.

"Dammit," he muttered, "what do I care if Lieutenant Laird Cragin flies to Mars on a tissue-paper kite?"

He was asleep before his head touched the pillow. . . .

"Leigh!"

The crisp voice of Elene Gayle awakened him, tense with a suppressed alarm. The tent was dim in the light of an oddly purple dawn. Pausing at the entrance of the tent, her face so gray and tired he knew she had not slept, she called urgently:

"That tornado is coming again. You had better see after your ship."

He tumbled out of the tent and saw her running ahead toward the long metal shed that covered her precious instruments. The dark ocean seemed ominously calm, and the sunrise above it was as splendid as the last.

Against it he saw what the girl, with obvious hesitation, had called a tornado.

It walked out of the flaming east—an endless spiral filament of silver, dropped like some cosmic fishing line from the depthless purple above the fiery sunrise. The foot of it danced across the sea. It moved by incredible bounds. And it was wrapped in a gray wisp of storm.

Leigh caught his breath and started running toward the plane that was standing unmoored on the long white beach where he had climbed out of her on the day before.

But this white funnel of destruction came with the same unthinkable velocity that he had witnessed before. Before he had moved a dozen steps, the white tent sailed over his head. The abrupt, freakish blast of air hurled him flat. His eyes and ears and nostrils were filled with coral sand.

For no more than twenty seconds the tempest shrieked against the black peak above. Abruptly, then, the air was almost still again. There was only a fluttering, queerly chill breeze from the east, following in the storm's wake.

Spitting sand and gasping for breath, Leigh staggered to his feet. The funnel of the storm, like the guide-rope, he thought, dangling from some unseen balloon, was bounding away into the gray west. Its sorrowful howling swiftly diminished.

Leigh turned ruefully toward where he had left the *Phoenix*. The battered old crate had been neatly flipped over on her back by the prankish blast of wind. Leigh shook his head and whistled a few bars of "Barbara Allen."

"Too bad, old girl," he muttered. "But, considering the state of

Tick's exchequer and the high cost of salvage, it looks like good-bye for us."

He turned to survey the station. The tent was gone. The supplies, cooking utensils and blankets that it had covered were scattered across the beach to the uneasy sea. The tarpaulins had been ripped off the long stack of crates; tumbled in confusion were red drums of Kappa-concentrate rocket fuel, long cylinders of oxygen, bright tins of gasoline, miscellaneous cases of food and equipment.

But where was the lady astronomer?

A sudden unreasonable alarm tightened Leigh's throat. He was too well seasoned, he kept telling himself, to get unduly excited over any girl—especially a female scientist who didn't like him anyhow. But he was running through the wrecked camp, shouting her name with a quaver in his voice.

"Miss Gayle! Can you hear me? Elene!"

"Dr. Gayle, if you please."

Her crisp voice came from the interior of the long observatory shed. Half the metal roof had been ripped off. Most of the equipment inside seemed to have been demolished by a huge boulder the wind had hurled from the dark cliffs above. But the slim calm girl, save for the disorder of her short yellow hair and a smudge of grease on her brown cheek, looked untouched. She was ruefully fingering a tangle of twisted levers and crumpled recording drums.

"No more barocyclonometer," she said. "But my visual observations make it imperative that we get in touch with the outside world at once. I believe my worst fears are justified."

"Well, Dr. Gayle," Leigh offered, "if you discover any need of my services, just say so."

"I doubt that you would be very useful." From the preoccupation of her voice, he knew she gave him less than half her mind; her eyes still measured the smashed equipment. "If you can repair your plane, you had better get away from here before tomorrow morning. Manumotu is an unhealthy locality, just now. And I'm afraid you'll find that the world has got more pressing matters to attend to than organizing relief expeditions to rescue stunt fliers."

"Thank you, Doctor." Leigh bowed. "I hope you can stand a shock. I believe the flying days of the old *Phoenix* are over."

"In that case"—her voice was still abstracted—"you had better salvage what you can of the supplies and equipment. After all, if what I fear is true, it won't make any great difference whether you ever leave Manumotu or not."

Leigh spent all morning stacking the tumbled crates and drums so that they made three walls of a tiny low shelter, roofing it with the torn tarpaulins, and collecting there the food and useful articles he found on the beach.

At noon, when he carried a plate of food and a steaming tin of fresh coffee to the girl in the observatory building, he found her covered with grime, laboring in tight-lipped silence with the starting crank of a little motor-generator. She waved him aside.

"I've no time to eat," she told him. "I've data of the utmost importance to send. It's urgent that I get in touch with Washington and our rocket laboratory at Alamogordo. And there's something wrong with this planet."

Leigh glanced at the balky mechanism. He set the plate on an empty packing box beside her and rolled up his sleeves.

"Did it occur to you," he inquired, "that, having made a living out of flying gasoline engines for the past ten years, I might know something about them? I see that your carburetor is smashed. If you'll eat your dinner, I'll make you a new carburetor."

Her face showed a weary relief. "If you can do it," she agreed.

While Leigh found tin snips and an empty milk can, she sat down on the concrete floor beside the packing box. She gulped the hot coffee, wolfed a sandwich of canned ham, and reached for another. In the middle of it, her yellow head dropped forward on her knees. Leigh heard a long sigh and knew she was asleep.

"Poor kid," he muttered.

Even the staccato *chek-chek-chek* of the little motor ten minutes later did not wake her. Leigh twisted the flap of tin that regulated the mixture, then swiftly checked the hookup of the shortwave transmitter.

He snapped on the receiver. Static snarled at him. An unfamiliar sort of static. The whining ululation of it was oddly like the howling of the storm that had passed. It rose and fell regularly.

Through it, however, he picked up some station—and what he heard stiffened him with fear. For a time he listened, absorbed; then suddenly he hurried to wake the girl.

"It's fixed?" she gasped, starting up. "I didn't mean to sleep—there isn't time."

He caught anxiously at her slim brown arm.

"Elene," he demanded, "what's happening? I was just listening. There's something frightful going on. What is it? Do you know?"

Her blue eyes stared at him. They were dark with sleep—and, he thought, terror. Quick and anxious, her low voice demanded:

"Just what did you get?"

"Storms," he said briefly. "Phenomenal storms. Unseasonable bitter cold. Ice storms even in the tropics. Tidal waves. One against the Atlantic seaboard has probably killed a hundred thousand already. Communications broken everywhere, of course. Panic increasing."

He drew her light body toward him.

"Something has gone wrong with the air, Elene. Do you know what it is? And when it is going to stop?"

Her head nodded slowly.

"I'm afraid I know what it is," she said. "My dispatches can't bring any comfort to the world."

"What is it?"

Her arm twisted free.

"No time to tell you now," she said. "I've got to talk to Washington and New Mexico. And to Laird Cragin—if he's still alive. Our work here has got to be finished tonight. After dawn tomorrow, there may not be any Manumotu."

Leigh gasped. "But—"

Hastening toward the radio, she paused briefly.

"I'll show you tonight," she promised him. "If the seeing is good enough for the telescope, and if we're still alive by then."

She had no more attention for him. He prepared food for himself, ate, and then spent an hour making the tiny little shelter more secure against whatever the girl expected to happen at dawn. And then, heavy with accumulated fatigue, he slept again.

The air was unwontedly cool on the beach when he woke, and another sunset of uncanny splendor flamed red to the zenith. He kindled a fire of driftwood, set out another meal, and called the girl. Sipping gratefully from a tin of scalding coffee, she gave him a brief smile.

"You have ability, Leigh," she told him. "Ability that has been wasted." Her dark eyes studied him. "Now, I'm afraid, you've very little opportunity left to make use of it."

Sitting silent for a moment in the dancing firelight, she began pouring the cool coral sand through her fingers into little white pyramids.

"If my deductions check out tonight," she said, "I'm afraid the creative functions of our present civilization are just about at an end. The planet will doubtless remain habitable for certain forms of life. Men may even survive in such places as Death Valley. But it will be a little strange if the human race ever recovers its supremacy."

"Tell me—" Leigh began.

She looked at her watch and studied the darkening eastward sky.

"In ten minutes," she said, "I can show you—show you why the earth is no longer a very safe place for nonstop fliers."

Leigh caught his breath.

He looked from the girl into the low, many-colored flames of the driftwood and slowly back again.

"Dr. Elene Gayle," he told her very gravely, "I feel that your frank comments have given me the right to express an equally candid opinion of female astronomers."

She nodded and looked back into the east.

"I haven't been following my profession altogether for fun, although I enjoy it," he told her. "I have been trying to save up two hundred thousand dollars. That would be enough to begin the manufacture of a gadget I have invented for the greater comfort of rocket passengers, and to build a home."

There was weary loneliness in his voice now.

"For hundreds and thousands of hours, cramped in the cockpit of the old *Phoenix,* I have endured fatigue and the need of sleep by dreaming of that home. Sometimes it is on a Florida key and sometimes it is in a little green valley that I have seen in the Colorado Rockies."

He looked at the girl across the fire.

"But always the most important thing about it was the woman who would live in it with me. I have had one in mind and then another. But none of them, Dr. Gayle, has fitted as well as you do—except, I must hasten to add, in certain regards.

"You must realize that I am telling you this just to make a point—since, what with crackups and your Stellar Shell, Tick Tinker and I have never had more than fifty thousand in a joint account."

A smile touched his lean face in the firelight.

"Physically," he told her, "you would do admirably. And you have intelligence, quickness, and, I believe, a sense of humor. But unfortunately you have other qualities that outweigh all these.

"Try to imagine yourself living a civilized life in a civilized home," he challenged. "You just couldn't do it. You wouldn't fit in—not with a schedule of forty-eight minutes a day for food.

"I hope I've made my point—that female astronomers who completely ignore the fact that they are women are just as out of place in a civilized world as extreme nonstop fliers."

Her first low laugh, and the light of amusement in her eyes, halted his argument. But her laughter grew higher and more breathless until she could not stop. Leigh saw that she was hysterical. He dashed a tin can of cold seawater into her face. She caught a sobbing breath and mopped at her eyes. With another glance at her watch, she rose abruptly.

"Come," she said in a shaken voice. "And let's see if there'll be any homes in the world ahead."

III

THE squat mass of the twelve-inch reflector looked through a slit in the end of the building that had escaped destruction. Its clockwork, beneath the humming of the little motor-generator, made a muffled ticking.

Visible in the dim light of a shaded bulb, the girl twisted the turret and swiftly set the circles. Before she had done, Leigh knew that her object was the red point of Mars in the east.

For a long time, sitting with her eye to the lens, she was silent. Leigh could see the trembling of her small hand, touching the control wheels again and again. At last she rose and stood staring eastward through the slit, rubbing at her red eyes. Her face was bloodless.

"Well?" said Leigh.

"It's what I thought," she whispered. "Mars!"

Leigh moved into the seat she had left. His eye found the ocular. In its little disk of darkness, a single star burned with changing red and blue. And the disk of Mars, still too near the horizon for good observation, blurred and rippled as if painted on a black flag flying in the wind.

Even for a moment of good seeing, when the image steadied, that mistiness did not clear. But he could distinguish the wide dark equatorial markings—darker, in fact, than he had supposed them—and the white ellipse of the south polar cap.

Two things he saw that puzzled him. Beside the polar cap was a little dark fleck—the darkest marking on the planet—that had an oddly purplish color. And across the yellow-red of the planet, toward it, was drawn a twisting silver thread.

The image blurred and shimmered again, and Leigh rose impatiently from the instrument. A little ache throbbed in his unaccustomed eyes. He turned anxiously to the girl.

"Still I don't understand," he said. "I saw a little purple circle, not far from the polar cap. And a queer white thread twisting into it. But everything looked hazy."

"That's just it," her tired voice told him. "Mars is hazed and dim with atmosphere—atmosphere stolen from the Earth. That silver thread is the other end of the tube of force that we have been calling a tornado—sucking air from the Earth across to Mars!"

It took a moment for the full meaning to strike him. Then swiftly he felt the shock of it run through his whole body, and he swayed a little, standing there.

"But," he muttered at last, "I thought there were no Martians!"

"It has been pretty well agreed that there are no intelligent inhabitants," she said. "My father gave up the last great attempt to signal Mars ten years ago. But since that time something has happened to Mars."

"What?"

"It just happens," she told him slowly, "that that purple-blue spot, under the other end of the vortex tube, is exactly where the object we called the Stellar Shell struck Mars, two months ago."

He stared at her, in the dim observatory.

"Then—you think—"

"The inference is inevitable. The Stellar Shell was a ship. It brought living beings to Mars, from somewhere. They needed a heavier atmosphere for survival. Across on Earth—now, at opposition, less than fifty million miles away—they saw the atmosphere they required. With the same science that built and navigated the Stellar Shell, they have reached across to take what they require."

Leigh caught his breath.

"Why didn't they land on Earth in the first place?"

"Why should they, if they are able to reach from one world to another to take what they want? Perhaps Mars, with half the Earth's sunlight and a third of its gravity, suited them better in other regards."

Leigh's brain was spinning.

"Stealing the world's air! How possibly can they do that?"

"I saw one clue," the girl told him. "The two satellites are very difficult objects, even with the refinements of this instrument. It was hard to find them. When I did, they were both much too far from the planet. They are plunging out into space, away from their old orbits!"

"And that means—"

"It means that they have been cut off from the gravitational attraction of Mars. I think that is because the gravitational pull of the planet, by a power of science quite beyond our grasp, has been focused into a tube of force that reaches fifty million miles across space to our atmosphere."

"That queer tornado?"

"Exactly." The girl nodded. "Our atmosphere is being drawn up it. It seems to race around the Earth every day, because the Earth is turning under it. The violent air currents it causes, and the very loss of air, generate the storms. The unusual sunsets and auroras are doubtless due to the incidental forces that form and direct the tube."

Beside the girl, Leigh peered up through the narrow slit. In the bar of purple sky, Mars was a baleful orange red point. His staggered mind groped for understanding of its menace.

"What can they be?" he whispered.

The girl's own voice was dry.

"Probably they are interstellar voyagers. They came from the south, quite possibly from one of the nearer stars in Centaurus. Beings capable of such a flight must be as far from our comprehension as we are from that of the ants. And we must be as helpless before them."

"Ants can sting," muttered Leigh. But a breath of night air through the slit seemed strangely cold, and he shuddered again. "When do you suppose they'll stop?"

Elene Gayle's yellow head shook in the dimness, wearily.

"Who knows? We could spare them half our atmosphere, and still survive in the lowlands, though the climate everywhere would be far more severe. Possibly they will be satisfied in time. Possibly the advance of the Earth in its orbit will break their tube of force—until the next opposition, two years away."

"Mars is a smaller planet," Leigh said. "They shouldn't need so much air."

"Because of the lighter gravity," the girl told him, "to get the same pressure and density, they would need more."

"So we are at their mercy? Is there nothing to be done?"

Her face was gray and hopeless.

"People will react in the ways predictable from their known characteristics," she said. "Most of the world's population has already been driven into a helpless panic. The governments that stand will try to mobilize their armies—against an enemy they will never even see before they die. Only a few scientists will try to make a calm analysis of the problem, try to discover what, if anything, can be done. I doubt that anything can be done."

IV

THE rocket arrived before midnight. Elene Gayle had been at the radio all evening, guiding it in with her signals, listening to the reports of planet-wide confusion and terror; and trying in vain to get some message through to her Foundation's rocket research laboratory on the New Mexico desert.

When the blue luminescent cathion jets streaked across the stars, Leigh ran with flares to light the beach. It plunged down at an alarming angle, a forward blast checked it in a great cloud of blue flame, and two men tumbled out of it.

The girl came with Leigh to meet them. The tiny gray man with a pointed beard was Dr. Laymon Duval, assistant director of the Foundation. And the tall slender black-helmeted pilot, he knew without asking, was Laird Cragin.

Cragin was limping, patched with bandages. The girl nodded to the older man, greeted Cragin with a warm handshake. His handsome face smiled at her.

"Sorry to be late, Gay," he said. "But the freak storm cracked me up in the Marquesas Islands. Had to wait for Dr. Duval, in another fireboat. But here we are!"

The thin grave voice of the older man cut in, anxiously:

"You are quite certain, Dr. Gayle—certain of the facts in your code message? You really believe that stellar invaders on Mars are robbing the Earth of its air?"

"Duval," the girl asked briskly, "do I make mistakes?"

"Fewer than any man I know," he granted. "What action do you suggest?"

"Return at once," Elene Gayle said instantly. "Get full support from the President and the War Department. Rush our experimental rocket to completion in New Mexico. Arm it. Send it to Mars to stop the loss of atmosphere."

Duval's gray head shook, doubtfully.

"The only thing we can do," he admitted. "But you know I have been in charge at Alamogordo. And I'm reasonably certain that our rocket can't be completed before the air loss, continuing at the present rate, will force abandonment of the project.

"Even," he added forebodingly, "neglecting the weeks required for the flight—"

"Anyhow," the girl broke in, "we must try. I'll fly back to America with you tonight."

"Tonight?" Carter Leigh echoed her last word. He groped instinctively for the girl's arm.

"I'll go with you, Elene," he said hoarsely. "I'll fly your rocket to Mars."

"Thanks, Leigh." She turned briefly toward him. "But you're not a rocket pilot." She turned back to Cragin. "Load fuel and oxygen. We've no time to spare."

"Hullo." In the smooth voice of Laird Cragin was no very cordial recognition. "So you're Lucky Nonstop Leigh? Well, it looks like you stopped, this time, in a rather unlucky spot. Better watch that storm at dawn. It cuts a swath around the world, every day, through the thirties. Perth and Buenos Aires already gone."

"Back in a moment," the girl said. "I've some notes to get."

Carter Leigh watched her run back into the dark, toward the observatory. Listening silently to Cragin, as he helped lift aboard a drum of the kappa fuel, he tried to hide the despair in him.

"Sorry, old man," Cragin was saying. "But I guess the job will fall to me. I've been test-hopping the experimental models. If Gay sends her rocket to Mars, I'll go with it."

Leigh caught his breath. Laird Cragin was no doubt a brave and skillful man, even now promising to face certain death for the world's sake. But suddenly Leigh hated him with a blind savage hatred. He trembled, and his fists balled up. Tears swelled in his eyes, until the girl, running back out of the dark with a thick briefcase, was only a misty shadow.

"We'd like to give you a lift, old man," Cragin's voice was smoothly regretful. "But this is only a three-place job. And we've no time—"

"Thanks," Leigh managed to say. "But I've got the old *Phoenix.*"

Elene Gayle paused to take his hand. Her fingers felt strong and cool.

"Goodbye, Leigh," she said briskly. "Sorry we must leave you. Watch the storm. Make any use you can of our supplies and equipment here. Get north, if you can, out of its track."

Leigh did not answer.

Duval was already in the rocket. Cragin swung the girl in, leapt after her, slid forward the curved transparent hatch. Leigh stood stupidly motionless until the pilot opened it again to shout a warning.

He stumbled back. The blue electronic exhausts bellowed out about him. His skin tingled. Ozone burned his lungs. Blinded, he covered his eyes. When he could see again, the rocket was a dim blue star, dropping and dimming, north-northeast.

Carter Leigh stood alone on the beach, softly whistling the melancholy notes of "Barbara Allen." Alone on Manumotu. It was midnight. Six hours, more or less, until that world-circling funnel should pass again.

Southward, beyond the dark loom of the peak, the strange aurora rose again. Sprays of green and orange crossed the zenith. That eerie light showed him the old *Phoenix,* lying upside down on the pale white beach. He plodded heavily down toward her.

"Well, old girl," he muttered. "Cracked up or not, it looks like we've got to make one more flight—unless we want to be picked up by that wind between the worlds."

He stopped abruptly on the coral sand. His eyes lifted swiftly from the battered old crate on the beach, up to the red and baleful eye of Mars, now well past the meridian. His mind pictured that silver cord from world to world. And his lips pursed for a soundless whistle.

"Well, why not?"

He stumbled to the old plane. His trembling hand touched the cold metal of her prop. His voice was quick and breathless.

"Why not, old lady?" he muttered again. "There's air all the way. And where there's air, you can fly with gasoline. It's thin and rough, maybe. But we've flown high before, and met our share of bumps."

He walked around the plane, inspected rudder and elevator.

"Quite a wind, I guess. But it will be behind us. And when you've got fifty million miles to make, you need the wind behind you!"

He peered in the darkness at the damaged aileron.

"The percentage may be a billion to one against us. But what's the difference? You're extinct as the dodo, old girl. And I am, too. And we're getting wise to the fact.

"After all, why not? She'll probably be flying to Mars with Cragin, if they get their rocket done. We might as well be there to meet 'em.

"Okay, Duchess! Let's get going!"

He knew it wouldn't be easy to get the plane righted and repaired and in the air in the six hours that remained before the wind funnel returned. But he had been in spots almost as tight before. There was the time he came down on the arctic tundra with a broken prop, and whittled out one of his own. . . .

Lucky he had the supplies and equipment at the abandoned station. He walked back for ropes and tackle. In an hour the old ship was on her retractable wheels again, with no more than incidental injury.

He started the motor, taxied the ship up beside the building where he could have electric light, and went to work on the twisted aileron. When that was crudely mended, he found half a dozen other necessary repairs—and still, for all he knew, there might be some hidden harm that he could not discover till the ship was in the air.

Four precious hours gone before the plane was ready to load. Two things he had to have—gasoline and oxygen. The air was already growing thin on Earth, but it would be thinner still in that tube of force.

Tumbling aside the drums of rocket fuel and cases of supplies, he began carrying crated tins of gasoline and pouring them into the empty tanks. Ten gallons at a trip. The empty tanks held three hundred, and he stacked tins behind the cockpit.

The Southern Cross tilted above the peak. Time fled away. He panted. Even in the chill of morning, he was drenched with sweat. Lucky the Foundation had been so generous with fuel for the motor-generator and the stoves. Lower octane rating than quite agreed with the ancient engine. But, if he started on the other, it would do.

The first ominous promise of dawn was in the east, before that task was done. Now the oxygen. He staggered under the weight of the long steel cylinders. Four of them. That was all he dared load.

Red tongues were leaping up in the east now; the vortex would soon be here. And he'd have to be high to meet it—as high as the *Phoenix* could climb. And even there, in the softer hands of the upper atmosphere, the odds would be overwhelmingly against him.

He made a last dash for an armload of food. He picked up a well-worn book of Keats, the name in it Elene Gayle. Who'd have thought that female astronomers read poetry? He climbed into the cockpit, and jammed his heel against the starter pedal.

While the starter motor wound up, he adjusted his helmet, tested oxygen tubes and reduction valve. He set altimeter and clock, put rudder and elevator trim tabs in neutral. He engaged the clutch, and the ancient motor caught with a roar.

Fine drops of oil on the windshield reminded him that it was in need of an overhaul. If there had been time and tools. . . .

"Crazy," muttered Leigh. "Off to Mars!" Against the roar, he began to whistle "Barbara Allen."

While the motor warmed, he pushed in the knob that flattened the pitch of the prop, and planned the take-off. The beach was now a ghostly strip of gray beneath that strange sunrise—too short for all the load the *Phoenix* carried.

He taxied to the east end of the beach, turned to face the uneasy west wind, plunged into it with a blast of the gun. The ship was far too heavy. Even with the stick forward all the way, the tail wheel still dragged. And the white spray, flying over black teeth of rock beyond the beach, was rushing at him.

But the tail came off the ground. The wheels tapped the sand, lifted, merely flicked the rocks beyond. Leigh caught a long gasping breath. He pushed the knob that started the wheel-retracting pump. The airspeed needle leapt ahead.

Over the dark unquiet sea north of Manumotu, he wheeled into the east. Moment by moment, the sky was flaming redder. He watched for the thread of silver in it, and trimmed the elevators to hold a steady climb.

He slid the cockpit cover forward. The air about him was suddenly calm. He felt a moment of relaxation before the crisis ahead. His eyes left the banks of instruments for a moment, found the worn little book beside him.

"Sentimental fool," he muttered. "Elene Gayle wouldn't carry dead weight to Mars."

He slid back the cockpit cover, hurled the volume into the shrieking wind. He was immediately sorry he had done so. He scanned the east again. Still no tornado. Would it fail him now?

The *Phoenix* was lifting twelve hundred feet a minute. The cockpit grew cold. He plugged in the heater units in his suit. His ears ached. His lungs began to labor in the thinning air. He adjusted the faceplate of his helmet, twisted the oxygen valve.

Then he saw the funnel. It came toward him like a swinging silver rope. Automatically, he banked the ship, flew straight toward it. He saw the dancing tip of it touch Manumotu, nearly six miles beneath. All the green vanished magically from its black cliffs, and a mountain of sea rose over them.

V

THE first blast of wind overtook him so violently that the ship stalled in it. The dead stick was loose in his hands. He shoved it forward, gunned the motor till the ship lived again, pulled it back.

He was trying to climb beside the silver funnel, to edge into it. But the blast of it caught him with a savage and resistless acceleration. The blood was driven out of his head. Darkness pressed down on him. He fought grimly for consciousness and strength to keep the nose of the plane ahead.

For an endless time he was suspended in that battle. His flying of the ship, the swift and delicate reactions that kept it alive and headed up that twisting bore of silver, his skill was half conscious. And he had no awareness of anything but life.

That killing pressure slackened at last, however. His strained heart beat more easily. He was aware of the plane again, creaking, twisted, battered—but still miraculously intact.

He turned up the oxygen, adjusted the prop to increase its pitch to the utmost, opened the auxiliary supercharger. The cold gas filled his lungs again, and he found awareness for things outside the plane.

It was the strangest moment Leigh had known. The curve of the silver tube seemed quite close, on every side. He knew that the air in it, and the plane, now had a velocity quite beyond conception. Yet it seemed that an odd calm surrounded him, and he held the plane, the motor at half-throttle, at its center without difficulty.

Though he knew the tube could be nothing material, nothing more than a vortex of etheric force, the walls of it looked curiously real. Almost glasslike.

Whatever they were, he soon knew that he had better not touch them. For a whirling stick in the air ahead had grown into a great black log—the stripped trunk of some mighty tree, snatched, he supposed, from Manumotu. He saw it spin into that glassy wall. Saw it instantly rebound in a thin dissolving puff of dust and splinters.

He twisted in the cockpit and saw the Earth behind him. Beyond the shimmering walls of the tube it was a mighty hemisphere, suspended in darkness. Gray and misty, patched with great circular areas of white cloud. The Americas were crowding near the rim of it—vast stretches white with unseasonable snow. Asia was invisible in darkness.

Perceptibly, the Earth diminished. It was odd, Leigh thought, that it looked smaller and nearer all the time, not more distant. The two Americas thinned and crept very gradually beyond the lighted curve of the world. The blur of Australia came slowly out of the night; the now invisible foot of the tube, he knew, sweeping destructively across it.

A steady pressure held him back against the seat. At first he had hardly noticed it. But it required effort, he realized, to thrust out his arms against it. The muscles of his neck were already aching.

It was that acceleration. Swiftly, ever more swiftly, that resistless suction was drawing him across toward Mars. So far, so good. He guided the plane around a good-sized granite boulder, drawn with him up the funnel.

The thing was incredible. Flying to Mars in the *Phoenix*—a second-hand crate that Tick Tinker had somehow wangled out of the city fathers of Phoenix, Arizona, six years ago. And the Gayle Foundation, with all its millions, had failed to fly its rockets even to the Moon.

But, incredible or not, it was happening.

After the tension and excitement of the last few hours, Leigh felt the pressure of a maddening monotony. He was already weary from loading the plane. And he found this flight the most exhausting he had made.

The air was too thin—so thin the motor coughed and stuttered, even under both superchargers. Even with the oxygen hissing steadily he felt faint and oppressed. And the cold was a savage thing. Even the heated suit failed to protect him.

Nothing changed. There was the ship and the silver tube. The Earth was soon a dimming point behind, beside the dimmer Moon, and Mars remained only a reddish point ahead. He ate a little, when the clock told him, from his scanty supplies.

Through the tube's pale walls space looked very dark. The stars were more brilliant, more colorful, than he had ever imagined them. But in their myriads he found it almost impossible to discover any familiar constellation. He felt lost amid their alien splendor.

He watched the clock. Its hands crept with deadly slowness. One day at last was gone. Another began. His body prickled painfully and then went numb with cold and fatigue. Sleep dragged at his brain.

But the shattering of the log had told him what would happen if his attention wavered.

"If nonstop fliers are extinct," he muttered once, "it's a good thing for them."

In his first wild resolve and in all the hazards he had met, he had not thought of what might happen next. But now, in this endless monotony, he had ample time to ponder the question: What will I do when I get to Mars?

He had a .45 autoloading pistol and half a dozen extra clips of ammunition with him in the cockpit—a relic as ancient as the *Phoenix*. How, with such a weapon, was he to cope with the science that had made this interplanetary tube?

Presently his fatigue-drugged mind recoiled from the problem, baffled.

Every dragging revolution of the minute hand seemed an eternity. But Mars at last began to grow beside the endless argent coils of the tube. It became a swelling hypnotic eye.

He shook himself in the grasp of monotony and sleep. But Mars stared at him. It was the ocher-red eye of that sinister intelligence that was stripping the Earth of air. He tried not to look at it. For its red gaze was deadly.

He woke with a start. The old *Phoenix* creaked and shuddered. The right wing-tip had touched the silver wall, and it was shattered. Twisted metal caught the air, dragged. He set the rudder to compensate.

But the tube had begun to widen. The current of air was slowing. A resistless force pushed him forward in the cockpit. Wind screamed about the *Phoenix*. She was plunging down toward Mars.

He cut the throttle, pulled the old plane back into a spiral. Savage eddies hammered her. She groaned and strained. Bits of metal whipped away from the damaged wing. More and more, it dragged and fell.

But Mars was swiftly growing.

He studied the clock. Just fifty hours since he climbed off Manumotu beach. He must have come fifty million miles. A million miles an hour—let Laird Cragin beat that in a rocket!

The face of Mars grew broad beneath him. The orange-red of it was white-patched, more and more, with the stolen clouds of Earth. But he found the white ellipse of the shrinking polar cap, the growing purple circle, above its retreating rim, where the Stellar Shell had landed.

Plunging down through the widening funnel that cushioned the air-jet from the Earth, he held the steep spiral of the *Phoenix* toward that purple circle. He would land in the middle of it, he resolved. And try to deal at once, as best he could with exhausted body and inadequate equipment, with the mysterious science of its creators.

A reckless determination rose in him. A wild elation filled him—the first man to cross space. He was the representative of all mankind, and he felt the strength of all men in him. He was invincible. If he must, he thought, he would make a bullet of the *Phoenix* and dive into whatever seemed the heart of the enemy's strength.

In his feverish excitement he wanted to push back the cockpit cover and yell. His lungs were burning. Then a glance at the barometric altimeter showed that it was registering. Air pressure was mounting again. He was suffering from oxygen intoxication. He partially closed the valve.

For a time a passing cloud hid the purple spot. With battered binoculars, he studied the surface of the planet beyond it. New lakes upon the reddish desert were black or mirror-like. The olive-green bands around them must be vegetation.

The cloud moved on, and he could see the purple spot again, perhaps only twenty miles below. A patch of dense purple jungle, the binoculars revealed it, far ranker than the olive-green beyond. Had the invaders brought alien seed to Mars?

A green line cut the purple wilderness, opposite the polar crown. And, in the center of the jungle, he saw curious glints and sparklings of green. The glasses picked out machines there. A colossal latticed tube thrust upward.

That mighty metal finger pointed toward the silver funnel, toward the far-off Earth. It was the finger of doom. It, Leigh knew, was the thing he must destroy. He tipped the shuddering old *Phoenix* into a steeper dive.

A long, long flight, his dulled brain thought, just to bring a man to suicide. But for all mankind, for Elene Gayle and her science, even Laird Cragin and his rockets, it was the thing he had to do.

Or so he had resolved. But the gesture was denied him.

That long green finger moved abruptly in the purple jungle. It swung down from the Earth, to point at the diving plane. The *Phoenix* was struck a staggering blow. If the power of that needle was the focused gravity of Mars, then a good deal of it, reversed, reacted on the ship. The impact battered Leigh into oblivion.

VI

WHEN Carter Leigh came back to consciousness, the plane was spinning down in a power dive. Her ancient frame quivered; scraps of metal were vanishing from her injured wing. The damaged aileron was jammed again.

He yanked at the stick, fought to bring her out of the dive. He stopped her spinning, and her nose came slowly up. Then he looked below for a landing place. Shallow lakes of yellow rain water patched the red desert. He found a level ridge that looked firm and dry enough, extended the landing gear.

But the air even here at the surface was still very thin. Lesser gravity made a partial compensation, but the landing speed must still be dangerously high. Still he came down.

The red ridge flashed up at him, and he tried to level off. For all his efforts, the dragging right wheel touched first, too hard. The plane bounced, veered dangerously. The bounce carried him abnormally high. He had time to get the plane half straight again. Another bounce, to which the whole plane shook and groaned. Next time, in spite of him, the injured wing grazed and crumpled. He fought to right the ship; but the good wing dipped, plowed into red mud, and was shattered to kindling. The fuselage rebounded, skimmed along on its side for a hundred yards in a spray of crimson mud, at last was still.

Leigh clambered painfully out of the wreckage. He felt his bruised limbs. Despite the stunning finality of the crackup, he found no bones broken. His helmet had been knocked off. His lungs had to labor, but they found oxygen enough.

Pale yellow-green shoots, pulpy and fragile, were pushing up through the wet red soil at his feet. He had come to rest at the margin of a wide shallow lake, that mirrored the drizzling sky. Far beyond, above the gentle red hills patched with fresh olive green, he could see a long low line of purple darkness. And his ears, after they had become accustomed to the silence, heard a continual distant roaring in the sky.

That roar was the wind of stolen air from Earth. That line was the purple jungle. Beyond it was the great machine of the stellar invaders, that had to be destroyed. Leigh, as wearily confident as if nothing were now impossible, set about that distant project.

He snapped the action of the old automatic, slipped it in his pocket. Two five-gallon tins of gasoline and the remaining cylinders of oxygen he made into a bale, padded with his thick flying suit.

On Earth, he could not have moved them. Even here, their weight was eighty pounds, and his own sixty more. The burden simplified the matter of walking. But the effort of breathing taxed his lungs.

The horizon was closer than it looked. He dwelt upon that fact for encouragement, and walked toward the barrier of the unknown jungle. The roaring grew louder in the sky. He reeled with fatigue. The slow drizzle of stolen moisture continued, interrupted with flurries of sleet. Cold sank into his bones.

He came at last to the jungle and super cactus. Jagged purple spines grew with a visible motion; they stabbed into the red mud, sprouted, lifted new barbed lances. It was a barrier too thick and dense for him to hope to cross.

Utterly disheartened, he flung down his burden. Mechanically, he ate a can of beans he had slipped into the pack. Then quite suddenly he slipped into sleep.

The slow thrust of a living bayonet wakened him, drenched and stiff with cold. His chest felt congested and breathing took a painful effort. He picked up his burden and slogged off westward through the red mud, skirting the advancing jungle.

It was in that direction that he thought he had seen the green slash. An exhausting hour brought him to it—a broad level pavement of some glistening, bright-green stuff. The surface was perfect, but the bank beneath it had a surprising look of antiquity.

This road came straight out of the north. It cut into the jungle, the walls of purple thorns arching over it. After brief hesitation—lest he meet its masters unawares—Leigh trudged in upon it.

The purple shadow of the jungle fell upon him. The roaring continued in the sky; cold rain and sleet fell endlessly. Leigh plodded endlessly on, ignoring fatigue and cold and hunger. Once he stopped to drink from a puddle on the road. A lancing pain stabbed through his chest.

A humming clatter startled him. He stepped off the road, thrust himself into the purple spines. A huge three-wheeled conveyance came swiftly along the pavement. The bed of it was piled with something pale green and crystalline—something mined, perhaps, in the equatorial regions.

Straining his eyes in the purple dust to see the driver, Leigh glimpsed only a gelatinous arm. That arm and a yellow eye and another translucent waving limb were all he ever saw of the actual invaders. Their nature, the motives and the course of their flight, the mysteries of their science, the extent of their designs upon the solar system—all these remained defined only by conjecture and dread. The invaders remained but a dark-limned shadow of the unknown.

The brief polar night was already falling when the truck passed. It was bitterly cold. The rain turned again to driving pellets of sleet, and heavy frost crackled over the roadway and the jungle spines.

The roaring overhead was louder now. A greenish glow filtered down the tunnel of the road. And at last, dead with fatigue, Leigh dragged himself to the edge of the central clearing in the jungle.

He perceived no source of light. But the surrounding wall of thorns and the fantastic structures before him were visible in a dull green radiance. He saw what must have been the remains of the Stellar Shell—a huge projectile, whose nose had plowed deep into the planet. Half its upper parts had been cut away; it must have served as a mine of the green metal.

Beyond it, swung between three massive piers, was the latticed tube, now horizontal, pointing across the pole toward the unseen Earth. Leigh caught his breath. Nerved with a last spurt of unsuspected strength, he staggered forward in the green shadow of the Stellar Shell.

Nothing stopped him. He swayed across a little open space beyond, dropped with his burden in the darkness between the three piers. His hands began shaping a basin in the half-frozen mud.

A hoarse coughing hoot, from some half-seen structure beyond, spurred him to desperate haste. He ripped open his bale, began pouring his ten gallons of gasoline into the basin. An unaccountable rasping rattle lifted the hair at the back of his neck. He heard a metallic clatter, nearer.

Fumbling desperately, he opened the cocks of the oxygen cylinders. The compressed stuff came out with a hissing roar, half liquid, half gas. It evaporated and enveloped him in a cloud of frost.

He turned the blue jets into the gasoline. Ticklish work. Before the invention of the cathion blast, gasoline and oxygen had been the favorite fuel of rocket experimenters. An efficient mixture of them, as makers of aerial bombs had sometimes demonstrated, had five times the explosive energy of nitroglycerine.

This wouldn't be a very efficient mixture. The gasoline froze into brittle blue chunks, and the oxygen was swiftly boiling away. The results were unpredictable.

Above the dying hiss of the jets, Leigh heard that rattle and the rasping hoot, very close to him now. He straightened in the thick white fog, and saw the yellow eye. A huge luminescent yellow pupil, fringed with a ragged membrane.

A pointed metal rod, glowing with strange green, appeared beneath the eye. It thrust toward him through the fog. Leigh stumbled backward; his numbed fingers found the automatic, fired into the yellow eye. It blinked and vanished, and the rod clattered in the fog.

Leigh staggered back to the end of the Stellar Shell and began shooting into his mud basin between the three great piers. At his third shot, the world turned to blue flame, and went out utterly.

The massive green wall of the cosmic projectile shielded him from the blast. And it sheltered him somewhat from the tempest that followed.

He came to, lying in the freezing mud, nostrils bleeding, head ringing. Dragging himself up behind the shielding barrier, he saw that all the great structures of the invaders had been leveled. The green glow had gone from them.

He started at some motion in the gray twilight; it was a gelatinous arm, waving slowly above a pool of mud. He emptied the automatic at it—and it sank.

Then the wind came. The interplanetary air-jet, now that the cushioning forces by which the invaders had sheltered themselves had been removed, came down in a shrieking blast. The mighty walls of the Stellar Shell were all that stood before it.

For half an hour, battered and half suffocated, Leigh clung to a metal bar in its shelter. The wind blew itself out abruptly, the last of the ravished air. The small sun rose warmingly in a sky suddenly serene, and Leigh slept half the day in its heat.

In the afternoon, still aching with weariness, he found the roadway again, and plodded back through the flattened jungle toward the wreck of the *Phoenix*. Hungry, bitter with loneliness, he began to regret that he had survived.

Some swift decay had attacked the fallen purple thorns, but the native life of Mars was thriving exceedingly. In the changing landscape, it was difficult to find the plane. When at last he reached it, he ate the solitary can of corned beef that remained of his supplies and then rigged up a directional antenna for the transmitter.

For several reasons, this last hopeless message was important. He wanted to end the fears of the Earth; wanted to help Tick Tinker; and he wanted Dr. Elene Kathrine Gayle to know that he had flown nonstop to Mars, usefully, with gasoline.

"Mars, calling Earth," he repeated. "Carter Leigh, on Mars, calling C Q, Earth. Landed here yesterday. Destroyed invaders last night with gasoline bomb. Anticipate no danger further loss of air. Inform Tick Tinker, New York, nonstop flight to Mars made with Zerolube oil. Now marooned on Mars. Good-bye, Earth."

He repeated that message, between intervals of sleep, until the little battery was exhausted. Then he set himself, wearily and without hope, to begin the life of the first Robinson Crusoe of space.

In a pot cut from the end of a gasoline tank, he made stews, queer-flavored but edible, from the fruits and seed of some of the native plants. Hoping to reach a less severe climate in the equatorial regions and driven by a desire to learn more of whatever lost people had built the road, he stowed all the useful articles he could salvage upon a sledge made from the elevator of the *Phoenix,* and set off northward along the straight green pavement.

The Earth, now drawing away from Mars, was a splendid golden morning star. Sight of it, in the frosty dawns when he could not keep warm enough to sleep, filled him with tragic loneliness.

One day he threw away the gun, to end his desire to use it on himself. The next he turned back along the road, and spent all the day to find it and clean it again. But when it was ready he put it on the sledge and plodded on down the glassy pavement.

He had counted thirty Martian days. With the slow advance of spring, and his weary progress northward, the climate had become a little more endurable. He was cheered sometimes by the sight of young, familiar-looking shoots—grown from seed borne upon that interplanetary wind.

But his body was gaunt with privation. He had a recurrent painful cough. Sometimes his meals from the Martian plants brought violent indigestion. The end, he clearly saw, would be the same, whether he used the gun or not.

Then the night, the incredible night, when he woke in his chill bed beside a smoldering fire, to hear the familiar rhythmic drum of cathion rockets. He saw a blue star following down the roadway from the south. Breathless and quivering, he sprang up to feed his fire.

Mantled in the blue flame of its forward jets, the rocket came down upon the road. His firelight showed the legend on its side: *Gayle Foundation.* It would be Laird Cragin, he supposed, another exile—

But the bare grimy yellow head that appeared, when its thick doors swung open, was the head of Elene Gayle.

"Greetings, Mr. Lucky Leigh," her brisk voice said. "And congratulations on the aptness of your nickname. . . . Are you all right?"

"Right as rain," he croaked hoarsely. "Only—surprised!"

"We finished the rocket." She was oddly breathless. "When the guns and explosives were no longer necessary, we loaded it with return fuel and supplies for a few weeks of exploration."

"Cragin?" demanded Leigh.

"There were two places," said the girl. "After we took off, I made him drop back by parachute." Her voice was suddenly very crisp. "I have the honor to bring you, Leigh, in token of the gratitude of Earth for your recent remarkable nonstop flight, the medals and awards—"

Her voice broke abruptly. She stumbled out of the rocket, and came running across the strange pavement to meet him. In his arms, trembling, she clung to him.

He staggered across that terrible land—alone

Nonstop to Mars

By JACK WILLIAMSON

Here is the record of Lucky Leith's incredible flight; how he piloted his ancient ship through the thunder between two worlds—to become the first Robinson Crusoe of space. A complete novelet

JACK WILLIAMSON
FATHER OF SCIENCE FICTION

John Clute

Obituary from *The Independent,* 13 November 2006

It seems that there was never a time when Jack Williamson, who has died at 98 after an active career extending from 1928 until late last year, was not the elder statesman of American science fiction. "If your father read science fiction," editor and novelist Frederik Pohl once wrote, "he very likely counted Jack Williamson high among his favorite writers." What now seems remarkable about this statement is that it was made in 1953.

But of course *Star Science Fiction Stories #2,* the anthology of original stories Pohl was introducing, was anything but a memorial volume; the early 1950s series to which it belonged soon became famous as a vehicle for the new blood writers who had begun to transform the science fiction genre after World War Two, and Williamson gained entry there, in Pohl's words, "as a sort of combination of revered old master and bright new star." He had in fact already re-invented his craft and his career more than once, and, almost magically, over the next 50 or more years, he continued to fill the double role that Pohl had assigned him: simply by surviving and remaining dauntingly active (he published at least 10 stories and two novels in the 21st century) he seemed somehow to guarantee not only the continuity but the inner youth and freshness of American genre science fiction itself. He had been there at the beginning (the very term science fiction was not invented until 1929), and his death marks at the very least a symbolic terminus for the intimacy of the old genre. Over the decades, most of the professionals in the field had met Jack Williamson personally; there are few professionals now alive who had not read him as a child.

John Stewart Williamson was born in Arizona while it was still a Territory, and grew up on various ranches and farms; his family eventually migrated by covered wagon to New Mexico, where he lived the rest of his life. His home at Portales remains a working ranch. In the early days, however, ranching was hardscrabble, and his father became principal of the local school, partly to make ends meet; young Jack—like so many boys attracted to science fiction in subsequent decades—turned into a lonely, unsocialized, bookish child. By the age of 20—later generations of science fiction writers also tended to start young—he was a published author, his first story, "The Metal Man," appearing in Hugo Gernsback's *Amazing Stories* in 1928. His first book, *The Girl From Mars,* a novella written with Miles J. Breuer, appeared the next year from a Gernsback firm. It was a very strange story; but the nascent genre of science fiction—in which Williamson soon became a major figure—was itself strange.

The densely packed 24 pages of this tale mix together cataclysmic super science—the humanoid civilization of Mars blows itself up with atomic bombs, and ray guns and resistant spheres of force and super intellects proliferate back on Earth—and a catastrophe-oriented understanding of psychology: the behaviour of the human family at the centre of the tale is dysfunctional at a positively Jacobean level (almost everyone is violently dead by page 24). The underlying message, almost certainly unintended by the young Williamson, was that the future would be a region of deep stress: that it would be no easy task for an American to live on the cusp of things: inheriting the whole world but having to make something of that inheritance. More than almost any of his contemporaries, Williamson had an instinct for depicting this cultural instability, never comprehensively articulated but patently present in his work. The protagonists of his 1930s stories seem almost to sleepwalk into the triumphs and disasters they are heir to. The wind of the future is in their faces, and at times it blinds them.

Williamson himself underwent psychoanalysis in the decade before World War Two, and clearly had his own demons to subdue. His early prolificness was indeed almost manic. Almost everything contained in the first six large volumes of his complete short stories (all that have been released to date) was published before writers like Isaac Asimov and Robert A. Heinlein entered the field in 1939 and began to transform it; in their dozens, these stories exhibit an inner agitation that he never wholly escaped, and which he conspicuously exhibits even in a very late tale like "The Man from Somewhere" (2003), whose title amusingly echoes his first book. This story, in which Williamson is clearly paying homage to his early work, sweepingly jams together time travel and black holes, and a numbing depiction of family and cultural dysfunction, into a vision of the irreversible self-destruction of the human race. Under the calm clear narrative voice Williamson invented as part of his assimilation of science fiction's new maturity after 1945 or so, this deep agitation persists—a sense that surface clarity must always wrestle with despair. Clarity as a fix for despair: this is not perhaps a bad description of the effect of the best American science fiction.

But there was more to Williamson than dread. In the 1930s, he began a series of exuberant and expansive space operas, the *Legion of Space* tales; in these stories his heroes—most notably the Falstaff-like Giles Habibula, according to contemporary polls the most popular continuing character to appear in 1930s science fiction—were in command of the action, and the future, and the universe. The science may have been minimal, but a little later, in the early 1940s *Seetee* sequence, he treated issues of genuine speculative science as well, incorporating into ample action sequences a sophisticated take on the possibility and implications of anti-matter, and other issues alive in the physics of the time. Almost simultaneously, he published in *Unknown* magazine the grim first version of *Darker Than You Think* (1948), a quasi-scientific but very dark treatment of werewolves as genetic throwbacks, an explanatory principle which has fueled seemingly innumerable horror novels ever since.

This novel would be his most famous, along with *The Humanoids* (1948), a tale in which he again uses the word android in its modern sense (he had invented the modern usage in 1936; later, in a 1942 story, he coined the term and the concept of terraforming; he was also the first to use the term genetic engineering in fiction); under its calm surface, *The Humanoids* expresses, once again, an agitated sense of tribulations to come; its examination of artificial beings, and of issues of Artificial Intelligence, is prescient. A late sequel, *The Humanoid Touch* (1980), carries the speculation further. These novels proclaim their smooth mastery of their form; by the late 1940s, Williamson seemed to have tamed his own personal demons, and to have translated his personal and cultural anxieties into art.

It was not to last. Though his private life seemed to be increasingly stable—he had married his childhood sweetheart, Blanche Slaton Harp, in 1947—by 1950 or so he began to suffer a severe writer's block, from which he did not escape fully for at least two decades. Novels and stories did appear, some in collaboration with writer and academic James E. Gunn, whose example may have helped persuade him to return at this time to higher education. He had attended classes at the University of New Mexico in 1932-1933 without graduating, but now took an MA at Eastern New Mexico University (ENMU) in 1957, where he taught from 1960 until his retirement in 1977, remaining Professor Emeritus until his death; in 1964 he took a PhD in English literature with the University of Colorado. His thesis was published as *H.G. Wells: Critic of Progress* (1973), and he won the 1973 Pilgrim Award for his academic work. His influence as a teacher was already extensive, and the growth of science fiction as an academic career choice is in part due to him. The annual Jack Williamson Lectureship Series, sponsored by ENMU, began in 1977, and continues. The Jack Williamson Science Fiction Library at ENMU, endowed in 1982, contains nearly 30,000 books and journals.

By the late 1960s, his writer's block had gone into remission. With Frederik Pohl, he wrote the successful *Starchild* trilogy (1964-1969), which inventively combines space opera and xenobiological speculation; and he soon began to publish what many readers think of his best work, releasing 19 novels between *The Moon Children* (1972) and his final tale, *The Stonehenge Gate* (2005). Notable titles included *Manseed* (1982), an updated examination of genetic engineering, and *Terraforming Earth* (2001), the shorter magazine form of which, "The Ultimate Earth" (2000), won both the Hugo and Nebula Awards. His later years were peppered with awards, including the Nebula Grand Master Award in 1975, the World Fantasy Life Achievement Award in 1994, induction into the Science Fiction Hall of Fame in 1996, and Grandmaster of the World Horror Convention in 2004.

Williamson's last years were successful but not untroubled. As he recounts in the 2005 revision to his autobiography *Wonder's Child* (1984, rev. 2005), his wife was killed on 5 January 1985 in an auto accident while he was at the wheel. But he remained exceedingly active on all fronts until early 2006. He carried his era with him to the end. That era is now finished.

—John Clute

APPRECIATIONS II

JACK WILLIAMSON
Patrice Caldwell

As a teaching colleague of Jack Williamson and his eternal fan, I am privileged to be among the people lucky enough to share with all of you a part of his extraordinary life. Whether at a convention or in a classroom, at the post office or at the kitchen table of his home, Jack Williamson was always the gentleman-gracious host, encouraging supporter of writers, delighted to have readers, happy to be in "the game" of publishing the literature he loved most. His keen eye and clear, precise style brought science fiction some of its most important words and ideas. Above all, Jack Williamson taught us all that the mutual understanding of science and the humanities can build new worlds, can terraform planets, and can make us all better stewards of our humanity. Jack told countless students, "May the force be with you!" Generous to the end, he would have wished the same to all of us. Everyone at Eastern New Mexico University joins me in thanking Jack Williamson for all he meant to us, all he contributed to our students and to SF. His was a life lived with an amazing grace.

— *Patrice Caldwell*

JACK
James Frenkel

Jack Williamson was so many different people, it's hard to know where to start. Science fiction, fantasy, horror. Classic pulp adventure writer, academic, SFWA President, collaborator, comic strip writer, world traveler . . . Jack was all those things. He was also perhaps the most durable SF writer of all time, and the most undeservedly modest.

Working with Jack was an experience that at first confused me as it probably confused others. He was so modest about his accomplishments it seemed unlikely that this could be the man who wrote those great stories—*The Legion of Time, The Legion of Space, The Humanoids, Darker Than You Think,* and so many more. From the very beginning, he was unfailingly thankful for anything and everything I did for him as editor or publisher. And he never, ever complained—he always focused on the positive, regardless the situation. In other words, working with him was like living a wonderful dream. Great, legendary author, easy to work with. That combination is hard to beat.

Jack was virtually the living embodiment of American science fiction: curious about everything—the future, science, technology, everything else; optimistic about people and human nature in general, in the face of the evil of the times when our country faced its deepest crises; hardworking and persistent in the face of personal difficulties. With his Jimmy Stewart-like self-effacing manner and his positive attitude he was one of the great treasures of the field, both as a creative force and as a role model to multiple generations of writers who looked to him for guidance and encouragement.

I edited his books for almost 30 years, and never would have dared dream our editorial relationship would have or could have lasted so long. And yet his novels were worth publishing, and in fact I thought they got better as he got into his late 80s and 90s. *The Silicon Dagger,* which he wrote at 90, has a scene that truly astonished me; when his protagonist discovers the dead body of the young woman who was going to tell him the truth about the deadly conspiracy in this contemporary thriller. The scene is so electrifying, so hot with suspense, so sharply written that I was mesmerized. I had never seen anything by Jack that was quite like it.

Whenever I talked to the Tor sales force about Jack, I would always describe him as an up-and-coming young writer. And people would laugh, I'm sure. But in many ways, he was always young, because he never stopped trying new things; he never lost that marvelous sense of wonder, his innate curiosity about the world, the universe. I sometimes think of him when he was seven, looking up at the vast bowl of stars above the covered wagon that carried him and the rest of his family to their New Mexico Territory home. I can just imagine him, looking up and imagining. . . . He was an explorer, of ideas, of scenarios.

He was also fearless when it came to trying new things. That wonderful photo of him on the cover of *The Faces of Science Fiction* is a perfect metaphor. There he was, in his cowboy hat, at his desk with his computer, in 1983. Even today some writers fear computers. But

Jack was using a computer early on, though he was in his mid-seventies when he got his first PC. And he was e-mailing 'til about a month before he died. He sent the final revision of his final novel, *The Stonehenge Gate,* as an attachment. Jack wasn't scared of technology. He was having fun!

When we were getting ready to publish that last novel, a reviewer for a major Southern newspaper e-mailed our publicist for the book: Was this book ghost-written? Did someone do a massive re-writing job? Who really wrote it? I answered truthfully: Jack wrote it himself; nobody ghost-wrote it (the thought made me laugh out loud; this wasn't William Shatner we were talking about), and nobody did heavy rewrites. Yes, Jack was 97. But, I admitted to the reviewer, he wrote the book when he was only 96.

I tried to badger him into writing another novel, because I knew that he was happiest when he was writing. He told me he would if he felt he had a big enough idea, but he never did. But he did write a bunch of short stories. OK. He didn't have a novel-length idea, but short stories—damn, he was only 97!

When Roger Zelazny asked for original stories for *The Williamson Effect,* a book celebrating Jack in short SF, fantasy, and horror inspired by his work and his life, many writers answered the call. My favorites were Connie Willis's "Nonstop to Portales," which playing off Jack's title "Nonstop to Mars," was a lovely, fond homage to Portales, New Mexico's most famous resident, a man who, as one character in the story notes, "invented the future." My other favorite was "The Mayor of Mare Tranq," by Frederik Pohl, in which Jack Williamson saves John F. Kennedy's life in Dallas and as his reward, gets to be an Apollo astronaut despite being older than the Apollo program's age-limit . . . and then achieves what every true-blue SF reader or writer would want, the establishment of the first lunar colony. Both stories were based in Jack's greatness of spirit and his stature in the field.

What a remarkable man, what a great, generous soul. With his passing, an era of science fiction has passed, for he was the last of the Golden Age SF writers.

But as I said when an interviewer just today asked me how Jack felt about being the last of his generation, I don't think he thought about it a lot. He was too busy thinking about the future, imagining new stories until the end.

—James Frenkel

THANKS FOR THE INSPIRATION, JACK!

Bradford Lyau

I had the opportunity to have known Jack Williamson for three-and-a-half decades. Given his wonderfully long and rich life, this probably makes me one of his recent friends. We corresponded in the 1970s and 1980s and what impressed me the most was that he took time out from his busy schedule to respond to each point I brought up. No generalities in his correspondence.

This is important as his book, *H.G. Wells: Critic of Progress,* became one of the major inspirations for my dissertation while a graduate student in intellectual history at the University of Chicago. Our correspondence during this period involved discussing differences of method. After graduation and while going through numerous teaching positions, we continued to meet at conventions and he rarely failed to ask me how the teaching went or how my new research was coming along. When we last met in 2002, at his annual lectureship in Portales, he told me that he wanted to congratulate me for an article of mine that he read back in 1989. What a memory, what a person!

Thanks Jack.

—Bradford Lyau

JACK WILLIAMSON

Rick Hauptmann

I first met Jack Williamson in 1987, when I discovered that I had just moved to the hometown of this science fiction legend. Not quite knowing how best to contact him, I sent him a letter introducing myself as a fan and suggesting that we might have dinner sometime. He immediately wrote back agreeing to meet me, and invited me over to his house for a drink first. We ate at a local restaurant, with both of us enjoying the liver and onions that evening. As I came to know Jack better, and we became friends, I discovered that this initial encounter with him was absolutely typical of the man. Not only was he a brilliant person and a wonderful writer, he was one of the most humble people I've ever met in my life, and he was always anxious to enjoy the company of his fellow human beings. I'm pretty sure that Jack did not have an enemy in the world, and he (almost) never had an unkind word to say about anyone. My life has been immeasurably improved by the opportunity I've had to be his friend, and the world will be a much lesser place without him. He will be sorely missed by all.

— *Rick Hauptmann*

JACK WILLIAMSON, 1908–2006, R.I.P.
Elizabeth Anne Hull

Jack was dear to me for so many reasons, not the least being that I knew him in the early 1970s, several years before I first met my husband, Frederik Pohl, so I could be certain that Jack was being nice to me for myself alone and not just as a courtesy to Fred. Our first encounter was one of those pure-chance meetings at an academic conference on teaching English; Jack and I had both risen early on a Saturday morning to hear the only session on science fiction on the entire four-day program. It was quickly apparent to both of us that the presentation was useless for teaching at the college level, but we fell into a whispered conversation in the back, the room during which I discovered that Jack had compiled a listing of course outlines of science fiction courses taught at the post-secondary level. He was willing to share it with me, as he did with so many others like myself who were eager to develop a course in sf and had few models in those early years to follow. Just the thing I needed to jump-start my syllabus!

I saw Jack fairly often—once or twice every year or two—after I began to see a lot of Fred. When we visited him in Portales, the two smokers, Fred and Blanche, would keep each other company while Jack and I went off on long walks across the fields outside his home, discussing our frustrations about caring so much for people we couldn't persuade to stop smoking. It was usually all I could do to keep up with Jack's brisk pace. Jack would make his special oatmeal in the overnight cooker, or share his latest batch of jerky, made from beef from his brother Jim's ranch. I also cherish the visits to the ranch itself, seeing the cabin where Jack first wrote fiction, with the rattle of snakes under the floorboards and meeting the clan, brother Jim and sister-in-law Nancy and their children Stewart, Betty, and Gary. When Gary married a woman from New Jersey, Fred and I had the pleasure of representing the Williamson side of the family by attending Gary and Christine's northern wedding celebration. Betty was the inspiration for one of the characters in a collaboration between Jack and Fred. Katie, Betty's daughter, is already developing into a fine writer before she enters her teens!

Jack's niece Betty tells me that Fred and I were among the very few that Jack invited to stay with him at his house; this was symmetrical because Fred and I seldom stay with even close friends or family as we travel. I was shocked and saddened when Jack lost Blanche in an auto accident without any warning, and worried that he wouldn't survive without her. I hadn't counted on his resiliency.

When I decided the best way for me to return to China after my first visit in 1981 was to lead a tour group of SF people in 1983, Jack was one of the first to sign up, along with Fred, Roger and Judy Zelazny, Bill Wu, and Charles N. Brown. We all walked on the Great Wall, and Jack found the whole experience so fascinating that he came with us again in 1991, when we were invited by our dear friend Yang Xiao for a World SF meeting. As a special perk, Yang Xiao arranged a visit for us to the foothills of Tibet to see the panda breeding station, where we were stranded for an unplanned extra day by rockslides. The army cleared most of the rubble, but we still had to leave our vehicles and walk over several of the slippery rockslides, mumbling to ourselves all the while, "Assuming we survive, this will surely be one of the most memorable events of our lives."

The trip on the whole was more strenuous for Jack than he had bargained for; he suffered with a heavy cold for most of the three weeks we toured. After the meeting ended, Suzy Charnas joined Jack and Charles Brown and Fred and me for an excursion to Hangzhou and Shanghai and Beijing, as well as up into Inner Mongolia. At one point, the men voted (against the women) to turn back to Hohhot, rather than complete our planned excursion into the grasslands. It was the only time I ever remember being disappointed in Jack, but I forgave him almost immediately. If only he had been feeling better at the time, Jack surely would have voted with Suzy and me to go on and see what lay beyond.

Jack was the Sara Lee of the science fiction world—nobody didn't like him.

—Elizabeth Anne Hull

Created on the heels of an unkind *New York Times* review of his novel *Seetee Ship* ("It is a pity that the quality of [Williamson's] writing is such that this 'space opera' ranks only slightly above that of a comic strip adventure"), the editors of the *New York Sunday News* selected Jack Williamson to create *Beyond Mars* as an exclusive strip to run in their Sunday supplement from Febuary 17, 1952 through March 13, 1955. Set in the "Seetee" universe, the storyline featured the adventures of square-jawed Mike

Flint and his sidekick, a vacuum-breathing, rock-eating lisping alien named Tham, operating out of their home base of Brooklyn Rock in the asteroid belt. While Mike lived with his mother (it was the 50s, after all) on their stellar homestead, their adventures ranged across the solar system. Illustrated by Lee Elias and displaying an amazing coloring job seldom seen in the comic strips of the day, *Beyond Mars* is remembered as one of the high-water marks of SF adventure in newspaper comics.

JACK WILLIAMSON
JACK WILLIAMSON
LIBERAL ARTS BUILD

JACK WILLIAMSON, PIONEERING SCIENCE FICTION WRITER, DIES AT 98

Dennis McLellan

Obituary from *Los Angeles Times,* November 14, 2006

His first science-fiction short story was published in 1928, a year after Charles Lindbergh made his historic solo flight from New York to Paris.

But well into the first decade of the next millennium—and nearly 80 years after "The Metal Man" appeared in an issue of the pulp magazine *Amazing Stories* when he was 20—award-winning author Jack Williamson was still turning out science fiction.

A pioneer of the genre and one of the longest-active writers in the field, Williamson died of natural causes Friday at his home in Portales, NM, said his family. He was 98.

"Jack Williamson was one of the great science-fiction writers," writer Ray Bradbury told *The Times* on Monday. "He did a series of novels which affected me as a young writer with dreams. I met him at 19, and he became my best friend and teacher."

Bradbury said he showed Williamson some "awful stories" he had written, "and he was very kind and didn't mention how terrible they were. He shaped my life; he was very quiet and unassuming and respected my dream and let me be awful for a long time until I got to be good."

Arthur C. Clarke, author of *2001: A Space Odyssey,* once observed: "I have no hesitation in placing Jack Williamson on a plane with two other American giants, Isaac Asimov and Robert Heinlein."

Williamson, who believed that "science is the door to the future and science fiction is the golden key," wrote more than 50 novels, including *The Humanoids, Darker Than You Think* and *Legion of Time.*

Nearly a dozen of his science-fiction novels were written in collaboration with Frederik Pohl, including *Undersea Quest, Starchild* and *Farthest Star.*

The 1949 novel *The Humanoids,* one of Williamson's best-known works, was a cautionary tale about the dangers inherent in the development of new technology: robots that were designed to be helpful to mankind became so protective of humans that they essentially became jailers.

"*The Humanoids* marked a turning point in science fiction and in Jack's career," said James Frenkel, Williamson's longtime editor. "Before that, science fiction had been a cheerleader for science and technology and really had not, for the most part, focused on the potential dangers of science and technology."

Samuel Moskowitz, author of the 1961 book *Seekers of Tomorrow: Masters of Modern Science Fiction,* wrote that Williamson was "an author who pioneered superior characterization in a field almost barren of it, realism in the presentation of human motivation previously unknown, scientific rationalization of supernatural concepts for story purposes, and exploitation of the untapped story potentials of antimatter."

As a faculty member at Eastern New Mexico University in Portales in the 1960s, Williamson launched one of the nation's first college courses on science fiction and fantasy writing, helping legitimize science fiction as a field worthy of academic attention.

In 1976, Williamson received a Grand Master Award for lifetime achievement from the Science Fiction Writers of America. He also received a World Fantasy Award for life achievement from the World Fantasy Convention in 1994. Four years later, Williamson received the Bram Stoker Award for superior achievement from the Horror Writers Assn.

But his writing career was far from over. His 2001 novella "The Ultimate Earth" won both Hugo and Nebula awards. Williamson's last novel, *The Stonehenge Gate,* in which a gateway between Earth and other worlds is discovered beneath the Saharan desert, was published by Tor Books in 2005.

Known as unpretentious and accessible, Williamson credited hard work and constant inquiry with helping him remain current as an award-winning science-fiction writer.

"I have a vast curiosity about our universe, our origins and its probable future," the then 95-year-old Williamson, who subscribed to numerous science journals, magazines and newspapers, told the *Albuquerque Journal* in 2004.

His early years seemed like an unlikely launching pad for a science-fiction pioneer.

The eldest of four children, he was born in April 29, 1908, in Bisbee, Ariz., when the state was still a territory. And when his family moved to eastern New Mexico in 1915, they did it in a covered wagon.

But his family's arduous farming life served only to feed young Williamson's fertile imagination.

"We lived on isolated farms and ranches, far from anybody, and when I was young I knew very few other kids; so I lived to a great extent in my imagination," Williamson, whose parents were former teachers, told *Publishers Weekly* in 1986. "Life would have been absolutely empty without imagination."

Reading an early copy of *Amazing Stories* magazine, launched in 1926, was a turning point for the teenage Williamson.

"Here were spacecraft taking off from other worlds, travel in time and all sorts of wonderful inventions!" Williamson recalled.

He spent a year writing short science-fiction stories, composing them in his head as he worked on the family farm, then typing them on an antique Remington typewriter borrowed from an uncle.

A few of his completed short stories were roundly rejected before *Amazing Stories* published "The Metal Man," which dealt with radioactive emanations from a form of intelligent crystalline life that turned all objects into metal.

Williamson received $25 for the story, which was illustrated on the cover of the magazine's December 1928 issue. Thirteen of his first 21 stories, published between 1928 and 1932, were illustrated on various pulp magazines' covers.

Williamson, who was home-schooled until he was 12, attended West Texas State Teachers College and later the University of New Mexico in Albuquerque but left before graduating.

Shy and introverted, Williamson later described himself as "a solitary misfit—as science-fiction fans in those days often were."

During World War II, Williamson served as an Army Air Forces weatherman and rose to the rank of staff sergeant. He served the final three months of the war in the Pacific.

In 1947, Williamson's first book, a reprint of his early serial *The Legion of Space,* was published by Fantasy Press. Its modest success—it earned him $750—helped persuade him to return to full-time writing.

That included creating and writing the comic strip "Beyond Mars," which ran in the New York *Sunday News* for several years in the 1950s.

Williamson, who finally received his bachelor's and master's degrees from Eastern New Mexico University in the late 1950s, began teaching there in 1960. In 1964, he received his doctorate from the University of Colorado with a dissertation on H.G. Wells.

He retired from Eastern New Mexico University in 1977 but later returned to teach courses in science fiction or creative writing on campus every spring until about 2002.

Williamson's 1984 autobiography, *Wonder's Child: My Life in Science Fiction,* won a Hugo Award for best nonfiction book.

"I've never written bestsellers or made a great deal of money at it, but when I look back, I've been able to spend most of my life doing something I enjoyed," Williamson said in an interview in a 1999 issue of *Interzone*. "It's an exciting time to be alive. I wish I could live another century."

Williamson, whose wife, Blanche, died in 1985, is survived by his brother Jim and stepdaughter Adele Lovorn.

APPRECIATIONS III

I REMEMBER JACK

James Gunn

I met Jack Williamson in 1952 while standing in line to register for the World Science Fiction in Chicago. I turned and recognized a face familiar to me from the backs of novels I had read and loved. "You're Jack Williamson," I said; Jack admitted that was true. Jack was 44, but had been a science fiction icon for more than half his lifetime, and had attended the first World Con in New York in 1939. I was 29 and had published eight stories. Chicago was my first SF Con—indeed my first contact with other writers and readers — but Jack greeted me like a brother in SF and never treated me as anything other than an equal.

Jack's wife Blanche had a sister married to a Kansas City dentist, who they visited once a year. At our second meeting he told me he had experienced writer's block and asked me if I would be interested in looking at one of his blocked projects. I was writing my first novel, *This Fortress World,* then, but I agreed to consider the materials he had accumulated for *Star Bridge.*

Jack sent me 50 pages of a first draft that described Alan Horn being pursued on a buckskin horse across a New Mexico desert and 150 pages of notes about the invention of a process to shorten the distance between the stars in a tube of energy called a star bridge. That process had created an empire called Eron (Jack's tribute to Roman history and the aphorism that "all roads lead to Rome"), biographies of the characters, descriptions of locales, and a future history. With Jack's approval I turned his materials into a novel published by Gnome Press in 1955. We made a grand total of $500, which we split between us.

The oddest thing, however, was that the novel kept getting reprinted here and abroad. One of those reprints was reviewed in the *New York Times* by Gerald Jonas, who called it "pure, classic science fiction," which "reads more like a collaboration between Heinlein and Asimov." At the SFRA meeting in 1976, Ed Bryant, seeing Jack and me in the audience, said he had been turned on to science fiction by reading *Star Bridge* and then, looking at Jack and me, said, "I'm not sure I thank you." A couple of months later, Samuel R. Delany told me *Star Bridge* had turned him on to SF as well. David Hartwell, when he was editor of Timescape Books, took me to lunch and we discussed novels of mine he might reprint. He said he'd like to reprint *Star Bridge* again, because he reprinted it whenever he changed publishers. The novel had, he said, a marvelous combination of "my youthful energy and Jack's experience." He had it wrong, I said: it was Jack's youthful energy and my experience. Jack was always young in spirit. He had traveled to New Mexico as a boy in a covered wagon and he never got over the wonder of it. That wonder (he called his memoir *Wonder's Child)* and the loneliness and social shyness common at the time among SF fans combined to create a troubled but literarily productive young man who sought for self-understanding from psychoanalysts and for companionship among SF writers and readers. Eventually he became, as he told me once, "part of the establishment," when he went back to college not long after we met, got his bachelor's degree and a master's degree from Eastern New Mexico University in 1958, and a PhD from the University of Colorado in 1964. He spent the rest of a happy life in Portales (except for Blanche's tragic death of a heart attack after an automobile accident in 1985), as a professor and emeritus professor at ENMU, creating one of the nation's first science fiction classes, its science fiction library collection, and an annual lectureship, and endowing them. In his later life the world of readers and students made it possible for the hard-scrabble child of wonder to become a philanthropist.

He was a long-time member of the Science Fiction Research Association, compiled the first catalog of science fiction teaching, and won its fourth Pilgrim Award. He was named the second Grand Master of SFWA (after Heinlein), won the World Fantasy Life Achievement award, was inducted into the Science Fiction and Fantasy Hall of Fame, served as president of SFWA, and was guest of honor at the World Convention of 1977. He always was open to new experiences (including world travel to the Soviet Union and China) and protean in his ability to shape his work to incorporate current sensibilities and the latest writing skills, including the unlikely characteristics of the New Wave, and he carried his abilities into his

90s, publishing a dozen stories (one of which won the Hugo and the Nebula) and several novels in his last years.

For many of his early years Jack struggled to make a living at his craft and survived. as many of his generation did, by minimizing expenses, living on the Williamson ranch when he could afford nothing else, and building a shack behind the family home to use as an office. But he lived to see science fiction grow out of the pulps into the fan publishing of classics such as his *Legion of Space,* and then into the mainstream press and finally into film, TV, and broad general acceptance. Sometimes, in the process, things worked out for Jack, personally and professionally. When his *Astounding* serials *Seetee Ship* and *Seetee Shock* were published as books in 1950 and 1951, a reviewer criticized them as "comic book stuff"; that led the *New York Daily News* to seek him out to create a Sunday comic strip, *Beyond Mars,* for which he wrote the continuity for three years.

Just a few days ago I e-mailed Jack that Mondadori Books in Italy wanted to reprint *Star Bridge* once more in Italian. The editor referred to "the extraordinary character of Alan Horn." I was reminded of New Mexico's plans to create the world's first spaceport for public use. In *Star Bridge,* Jack called his imaginary New Mexico spaceport "Sunport." In honor of everything he stood for and everything he imagined, New Mexico should call it the Jack Williamson Spaceport.

Isaac Asimov told me once that "science fiction writers and readers didn't put a man on the moon all by themselves, but they created a climate of opinion in which the goal of putting a man on the moon became acceptable." Jack considered spaceflight the central myth of science fiction, just as the Trojan War was the central myth of the Greeks. Wouldn't it be appropriate to honor the man who helped turn the myth into reality?

—*James Gunn*

JACK WILLIAMSON

Joe Haldeman

One of my favorite memories of Jack Williamson was when he asked Robert Silverberg's advice about long term investment. Bob tactfully asked how old Jack was, and he said 75. But most of his relatives had lived into their nineties—and you can't be too careful.

Jack knew he couldn't live forever. He was at peace with mortality for many years, though I think he did want to make three digits, and had a better chance than most of us.

He was devastated when he lost his dear wife Blanche in an auto accident in 1985, after almost forty years of marriage. We were all so proud and glad when he pulled out of that dismal time and started writing again.

What a sweet guy. It's funny to think that Gay and I knew him more than 40 years, and that was far less than half his lifetime. The last time I saw him was three or four years ago, sitting in the Portales living room having a glass of wine with him, talking about asteroid mining and gravitational lensing in globular clusters, which was not unusual for Jack. His mind was sharp although his strong body was starting to give out.

About 20 years ago, we were with Jack at the Jet Propulsion Laboratory in Pasadena, watching the first close flyby pictures of Saturn come in. Gay and I ran into Carl Sagan, who obviously had had his fill of those "sci-fi" people and was rushed and dismissive—until Jack came down the stairs to say hello. That turned Sagan into a fan again himself.

He was a generous man in every sense of the word, respected by his peers—insofar as any of us could be peers!—and adored by his students at the university. Gay and I treasured the times we went with him out to the family ranch, where his brother's family would literally kill the fatted calf for Jack's SF friends, and four or five generations would sit around and talk of cabbages and kings. Listening to Jack and Jim talk about the old days was like being a fly on the wall of a time machine.

He published science fiction stories in each of nine decades. We won't see his like again, ever.

—Joe Haldeman

JACK WILLIAMSON
Greg Bear

Jack Williamson has been part of my life in SF since my beginning years, rising like a sequoia in a forest—one of our finest examples of how to conduct a life and a career, of how to write, how to pioneer for all who came later. The times I met him—at the Jet Propulsion Laboratory, at seminars, at conventions, in Portales—stand out for me. His humor, his courtesy, his obvious, intense, but not aggressive intelligence, and the sense that despite a historical difference in our ages, he treated me like one of the boys.

Whenever I start to get cocky and think I've come up with a new idea, I get a slight prickle on the back of my neck and go rushing to my shelf of Jack Williamson novels and stories. More times than I can count, I've found Jack did it first.

In 1977, in the *Los Angeles Times,* I paid homage to many of the authors and books that contributed to the world of space opera and—by extension—to a hit movie of that year, *Star Wars.* Jack was at the top of that list.

On significant occasions, we exchanged notes and thoughts on what it meant to be president of SFWA. I listened carefully.

I had the honor to share with Jack the Robert A. Heinlein Award earlier this year. Since Jack actually taught Mr. Heinlein a few things about writing, I knew I was playing sidekick, but I was very, very pleased, and regretted he could not attend the ceremonies.

As a physical presence, he could have starred in any number of movies as a prototypical gentleman rancher—a somewhat more homespun Jimmy Stewart type—but instead, he decided to write and to set his eyes on the stars, on the farthest reaches of the imagination—and he wrote, and speculated, and published, almost to the very end. More than three quarters of a century.

Wow.

By writing, and thinking, and being who he was, Jack Williamson changed my life. He changed us all.

—*Greg Bear*

THE DEAN

Mike Resnick

Jack Williamson was among the first science fiction writers to befriend me when I was breaking into the field almost 40 years ago. He was definitely the first to treat me not only as a friend, but as an equal and a peer, which made me feel he'd made a terrible mistake (and, in truth, *still* makes me feel so). He was so friendly, so giving, so approachable, that he always seemed to be completely unaware of the fact that he was, well, *Jack Williamson.*

He won the Hugo in 1984 for *Wonder's Child,* the first writer ever to win that most coveted award with an autobiography. One of my proudest editing achievements is that I got him to expand it, add another two decades to bring it up to date, add his diary from World War II, and also include a batch of photographs.

Like many of Jack's friends, I was flown out to Portales for a Williamson Lectureship. What impressed me the most was not the beautiful buildings, or even the outstanding science fiction collection in the library, but the credentials of many of the professors and assistants I met there. They were from Harvard and Yale and Columbia and Stanford and the like, and when I asked them why they'd chosen to work in a little out-of-the-way place like the University of Eastern New Mexico, the answer was always the same: they'd been reading Jack Williamson all their lives, and they'd have gone to New Mexico, or Burkina Faso, or to any place short of hell itself to work with him.

When it came time to do a "tribute volume," a collection of stories set in Jack's various universes and futures, I was one of those Jack invited into the book. I did a humorous little piece, a takeoff on his classic *Darker Than You Think,* in which the narrator winds up eating Jack Williamson. He got a real kick out of the fact that from that day on, I always introduced him to audiences as a man of exquisite taste. Which, all humor aside, he was.

I think the highest compliment I could pay him—and I've said it a number of times in a number of venues—is that he remains the only author in my experience who continued to improve with every decade. I can't think of any higher praise than that.

When you're 98 years old, your death doesn't come as much of a surprise, but that doesn't take the sting off it. Jack embodied just about all of science fiction's history in a single man and a single lifetime, and we're going to miss him for a long time to come.

—*Mike Resnick*

JACK WILLIAMSON

Walter Jon Williams

At some point in the 1970s, I'd heard Jack Williamson was going to be guest of honor at a SF convention in Denver. So of course I went.

I met Jack, which I'd been hoping I'd do, and we chatted, and the upshot was he bought me dinner, and we had a long and pleasant conversation.

I should point out that at the time I wasn't a published author, or a well-known fan. I wasn't much of anybody. I was a college student who had come to see Jack Williamson, and that's about it.

I don't remember what we talked about. I have a horrid feeling that I probably talked about myself a great deal. Jack was a good listener, and a good storyteller, and had a lot more interesting things to say than I would have, but he wasn't the sort to put himself forward—and alas, I am.

But there you go. Jack was kind, polite, generous, and a natural teacher. He was willing to listen to a young stranger drivel on about whatever interested him.

Years later I asked Jack if he remembered this conversation, and he didn't. I wasn't surprised—this was only one of many acts of kindness and consideration that Jack performed over the years, and he couldn't possibly remember them all. But I remember it very well—firstly, because any time that you spend with Jack is memorable; but more than that, it was the first time a member of our profession—and furthermore a man whose work I had been reading and admiring for most of my life—had thought I was worth talking to.

That conversation was an important event in the long chain that's led to me being the person I am, an actual honest-to-God colleague of Jack Williamson, with books of my own sitting on the stands next to his, telling an audience about the part he played in my life.

I'd like to mention another encounter with Jack, maybe a decade later. That year the World Science Fiction Convention was in Atlanta, and Jack and I both attended. We were on the same plane, though we didn't know it until after we'd disembarked.

Let me tell you what happens when you disembark at the Atlanta airport.

You leave the plane and walk along the jetway to the terminal, where you get on this kind of moving sidewalk that takes you to a moving stairway that leads down to a subway stop. And then the subway pulls in, and you get on board. There is no actual subway operator; it's all automatic. A machine voice tells you to stay back from the doors, and that the subway car is about to move. And then you zoom along on the subway till it gets to the main terminal, when a machine voice tells you that you can disembark, and you get out and stand on a moving stairway that takes you to an upper level.

Once there you stand by this giant automated shiny metal lazy susan, which eventually delivers your luggage off an automated conveyor belt. And it was while waiting for my luggage that I noticed

Jack standing across the lazy susan from me, standing and waiting for his luggage like everyone else.

And I realized that what I'd just experienced was a part of the world that Jack Williamson had built in his head and in print starting in 1928. The world he had built in his head and heart had come true in time for him to live it.

From the Mexican Revolution to the Digital Revolution, Jack was there, giving us all his special brand of foresight, optimism, and invention.

May we all live our dreams as Jack did.

I'm going to really miss him.

—Walter Jon Williams

JACK WILLIAMSON
Stephen R. Donaldson

Other people are better qualified than I to discuss Jack Williamson's vast body of work—although no one could fail to notice his restless intelligence and unflagging imagination. And I'm sure that other people have been on many more panels with him than I have, sharing his insights, his camaraderie, and his puckish sense of humor. But I've had the privilege of just "hanging out" with him at conventions, around the ENMU campus, in his home. So I know from experience that he was one of life's true gentlemen in every sense of the term, including the best: a gentle man. "In company," as it were, he was perceptive without being judgmental, keen-witted without being hurtful, and self-contained without being either aloof or stilted. Generous with praise, and utterly unwilling to denigrate (sometimes under extreme provocation). Self-deprecating. Playful. In fact, it's a cause for wonder that his probing mind and his kind nature were able to co-exist harmoniously in the same person. With his passing, a very human miracle has gone out of the world.

—Stephen R. Donaldson

JACK
Michael Swanwick

It's his voice I'll miss most—that warm and gentle and polite and courtly voice, and the simple kindness at its core.

I introduced Jack Williamson at a Worldcon panel once by giving a decade-by-decade thumbnail sketch of his career. "In the 1920s, he sold his first story. In the 1930s . . . 1940s . . . 1950s . . . 1960s . . . 1970s . . . 1980s . . . 1990s . . ." There was a significant accomplishment in each decade—and his second Hugo Award was still ten years away. I came to the end and, turning to Jack, said, "And my question is—can I do this too?"

But of course I couldn't.

Jack Williamson's career was unique. It embraced all of modern science fiction. While he was alive, our history was not an abstraction but a matter of real writers slamming words down on paper, playing with ideas, trying to make a living from what they loved best. Only one man lived through that enterprise from its raw beginnings up until . . . well, up until just a moment ago.

I thought he could go on forever.

Against all logic, his death comes as a shock. It was just so damned *right* that Jack should be with us. He'd earned it. His presence ennobled us.

Marianne and I went to two of the Williamson Lectureships, the first because I was a guest and the second because we'd so greatly enjoyed the first. One of the many astonishing things about Jack's life was that he was honored in his home town of Portales, New Mexico. They knew what they had while he was still with them and, God bless them, they weren't shy about letting him know it.

On our first visit, we made the world's shortest pilgrimage from the farmhouse on the Williamson Ranch through the back yard, over the fence, and to the writer's shack that Jack had built half a century before. Fred and Joan Saberhagen were with us and, knowing that at one point Jack had considered giving up writing and making his living as a carpenter, we examined every joist and join with a critical eye. It was all, like his fiction, solidly crafted. Finally, Fred nodded and said, "Yep, I'd hire him." Nobody needed to be told that his words had a metaphoric as well as a literal meaning.

In his final years, as Jack's health waned, his voice grew progressively weaker. You had to lean close and listen hard to hear anything at all. But it was worth it, because he had a quick wit combined with a generous heart. At the noisy post-Lecture party at his house, you'd glance across the room and see Connie Willis or Charles Brown bent over almost double by his wheelchair, ear almost to his lips, listening. And laughing.

Now he's gone. Some will have it that he's dead. But the truth is, he's just gotten quieter. If you listen hard enough, you can still hear his voice.

—Michael Swanwick

JACK WILLIAMSON

Kristine Kathryn Rusch

Æon Speculative Fiction, issue #9

The last few years have been hard on the SF genre. We've lost some of our best writers, and in November, we lost not only one of our best writers, but one of the best people I've ever known: Jack Williamson.

Jack died in Portales, New Mexico, at the age of 98. He arrived in New Mexico ninety years ago in a covered wagon. He lived to see the space program. Heck, he lived to be invited to the launches of various spaceships.

Jack wrote eight novels after he turned 90. He published his first short story in 1928, for Hugo Gernsback's *Amazing Stories*. Jack wasn't just a pioneer in the Old West, he was a pioneer in science fiction—and he wrote some of the classics of the genre. (My favorite is his non-SF novel, *Darker Than You Think.)*

Jack was the kindest man I've ever met. Even in a critique session, he refused to say something negative. He made certain he said something kind *and true* about the work before him. I've been in critique sessions with Jack where the nicest thing he could say about a writer's manuscript was "beautiful typing." But he would say that, at least, and the writer would leave happy.

But I don't want to write sorrowfully about Jack. Jack told friends a few days before he died that he was ready to face the next adventure. He was looking forward—which Jack always did.

In March of 2001, my husband Dean Wesley Smith and I were invited to be speakers at the Williamson Lectureship. Eastern New Mexico University in Portales put on the lectureship every year (including this past year) since Jack retired his teaching post there. The year we came, we were joined by SciFi.com's Scott Edelman and the marvelous SF writer, Connie Willis.

The lecture hall at ENMU was full of young students and a few recognizable faces (SF writers, well-known scientists, SF scholars and some old friends). The discussion, on the future of science, was lively—one of the most interesting I've ever been involved in.

And what struck me then—and still amazes me now—is that the most informed person in that room about the future of science was none other than Jack himself.

Too often, I've been around elderly folk who talk about the old days or refuse to pay attention to new things because they're happy with their rut. My own beloved grandmother refused to use a new television the family had bought for her because she preferred her old tube television (although she did think Mr. Coffee was the best invention ever).

When I met Jack more than twenty years ago, he was already elderly by anyone's definition. He still stood taller than me in those days, but his body had bent into a question mark. Over the years, the question mark remained, but by the end, I could look down on his wispy white hair. Jack's body grew older, but his mind never did.

The questions in 2001 were all about the future—and many of them came from Jack. He studied, not just as a science fiction writer trying to keep up with an element of his craft, but with the enthusiasm of a man who loved life in all its incarnations—who had seen many of those incarnations—and knew that there were wonderful things to come.

Even at the age of 93, he was still enthusiastic about what was ahead.

When I read his most recent novel, *The Stonehenge Gate,* in its *Analog* serialization, I realized that Jack saw life as a broad continuum. People left, but the continuum remained. Life, for him, was a stream, constantly changing, but always moving, always interesting.

Jack was, and is, perhaps our purest SF writer. *The Stonehenge Gate* is adventure fiction with a touch of the pulps where Jack got his start, but it is also a meditation on individual lives and love and the influence a person can have, not just on his own culture, but on one he couldn't even imagine when he was a child.

And that's Jack. As a human being, he had a tremendous impact on me. As a teacher, he gently molded generations of young minds. But as a writer, he influenced people the world over—for nearly eighty years.

What a legacy.

We would be remiss, in discussing the life of this very important man, if we do not discuss the future. For the future was the source of his inspiration and the place he boldly walked toward.

Even as he faced his last great adventure.

So look toward the future. Help preserve it for those who'll come after us.

Do it to honor one of the great pioneers of the future: Jack Williamson.

Whom I will miss more than I can say.

—Kristine Kathryn Rusch

JACK WILLIAMSON

David Brin

One of the sweetest and most genuine human beings, a man whose life and vision spanned farther than most of us can even dream, Jack Williamson also seemed to have fans in *very* high places, who wanted him to keep writing, which he did till age 97. Like many others, I thought he was invulnerable.

Jack helped pioneer the literary genre which deals courageously with frontiers and change; but that wasn't the keynote. Nor the relentless example that he set, in both his work ethic and optimism. Nor even his unfailing kindness, with never a word of malignant gossip toward anyone else.

No, I believe the most striking thing about Jack Williamson was the overall work-of-art that his modest life became over the years. Born in the Sierra Madre, he was the real treasure of Eastern New Mexico. No doubt the real reason for all those Roswell visitors. Looking for autographs, I bet.

Jack carved his own memorial, in words and ideas, but also in so many authors and readers who consider ourselves to be his daughters and sons.

—David Brin

JACK WILLIAMSON—SUPERHERO

Kevin J. Anderson

I've known Jack Williamson since before my first novel was published, almost 20 years ago. He was quiet, unassuming, and a genuine giant everywhere he went. For as long as I can remember, Jack received a standing ovation when he appeared at events. The SF field recognized his impact and influence, and we weren't shy about letting him know it. I was particularly delighted to be part of a surprise at Bubonicon in Albuquerque one year: For a panel innocently titled "The Works of Jack Williamson," Jack arrived expecting a handful of fans, only to find the room packed. A representative made a showy presentation from the Mayor of Albuquerque recognizing Jack's achievements and declaring that to be "Jack Williamson Day." Jack was stunned and choked up. "I think I'm going to cry!" he said (and he did—and so did just about everybody else).

But my favorite memory of Jack involves a bunch of old superheroes. In a project for DC Comics, I wrote a six-issue series of the *Justice Society of America* set in the 1940s. I proposed centering the story around pulp SF writer Jack Williamson being sent out by Hugo Gernsback to write superhero tales for *Amazing*. DC said OK, but only if I could get permission from *Amazing* and Jack himself.

Johnny Wilson, who owned the trademark for *Amazing,* was very happy with the idea, and Jack—well, he was practically walking on air when I asked him. "I used to read all those comics in the '40s," he told me. The thought of having himself in a comic alongside Green Lantern and Flash thrilled him. I wrote the scripts, in which Jack took geeky Johnny Thunder under his wing, being his mentor so Johnny could get a story published in *Amazing*. I sent Jack a copy of each issue as soon as it was published, and I received charming letters back from him as he read the comics. "Oh boy, looks like I'm in trouble now!" or "Thanks for another wonderful installment of my adventures with the superheroes. They amaze my friends."

When the six issues of *"JSA: Strange Adventures"* were published, I asked Jack to write an introduction to the series which is reprinted on the next pages.

He was always gracious, personable, imaginative, and a perfect gentleman. It didn't matter what company he was in, Jack Williamson was the real superhero.

—Kevin J. Anderson

JSA INTRODUCTION
By Jack Williamson

Who created *The Justice Society of America?* An interesting question, because so many gifted writers worked to give us the legendary superheroes, too many of them to name. The best answer is Julius Schwartz, "Julie" to his friends. As an editor at National Publications, later renamed DC Comics, he made a million friends. I'm happy to have been one of them.

After forty years of inventing new ideas and coaching writers and artists, he said he'd written only three scripts, but he had a genius for recreating fading or failing heroes. Beginning with the Flash, he brought new life to an army of mythic heroes: Superman, Batman, Green Lantern, Hawkman, and the Atom, as well as the Justice League. His success inspired the rival firm, Marvel Comics, to invent Spider-Man, the Fantastic Four, the Incredible Hulk, as well as others. Not many men have given so much to the popular culture.

Julie was born in the Bronx in 1915, attended Hebrew schools, and graduated from college with a Bachelor of Science degree in 1936. He was a devoted science fiction fan and a bridge fanatic when I met him that year on a visit to New York. Active in science fiction fandom, he was editor of several fan magazines; one of them, *The Science Fiction Digest,* ran until 1934. He and his friend Mort Weisinger founded the Solar Sales Service, the first science fiction agency. He bought it from Mort, selling the work of such writers as Ray Bradbury, Edmond Hamilton, and H. P. Lovecraft.

During World War II, Julie was turned down for military service. One of his Solar Sales clients told him of a job opening at National Publications. He had never read the comics, but on his way to the interview he picked up three and read them on the subway. He was hired in February, 1942.

He had found his life career. By 1970 he was editing the *Superman* family of comics, and he handled the revival of Captain Marvel in

1973. A good many of my friends in science fiction, including Edmond Hamilton, found second careers writing scripts for him. I never did, though I created and wrote the "Beyond Mars" strip for the New York *Sunday News*. Drawn by Lee Elias, who had worked with Milt Caniff, it ran for three years.

I kept in touch with Julie. While I was president of the Science Fiction Writers of America, I heard that Jerry Siegel and Joe Schuster had received only $140 for the creation of Superman, the first and greatest of the superheroes. In spite of objection from snobs who felt that comics were beneath us, I arranged to give them a special award. They were not able to attend. Julie accepted it for them, gave me a tour of the DC offices, and introduced me to the staff. Later, I believe, they received a more generous compensation.

Julie retired in 1985, but he was retained as a consultant to DC Comics, serving as a sort of roving ambassador. Popular at conventions, his lectures were brief histories of science fiction, illustrated with slides of his old friends in the field. Those included nearly everybody. He despised the Batman films, but they did increase the circulation of the magazines.

I don't think I ever met his wife, Jean, who was not involved in fandom. A devoted couple, they had a daughter. He outlived both of them, dying in 2004. The comics of today are a monument that should fill him with pride. Nobody else did more to build it.

Born in the early 1930s, comic books had found millions of eager young readers, but circulations dwindled after World War II. To hold them publishers turned to the violence and gore. William Gaines' E. C. Comics *Vault of Horror, Crypt of Terror,* and *Haunt of Fear* won a lot of readers but set off a storm of public criticism. That reached a high point in 1954 with an attack from Dr. Fredric Wertham, a German-American psychiatrist. Obsessed with a notion that they were corrupting children and inciting juvenile crime, he wrote a sensational book, *Seduction of the Innocent,* and gave testimony before a Senate subcommittee.

His charges were as extreme in their own way as the E. C. Comics. He testified that comics "create an atmosphere of deceit and cruelty." He attacked Superman for "arousing fantasies of sadistic joy in seeing others punished while you yourself remain immune." At the hearing Gaines tried to defend his magazines.

"Good taste," he said, was his only criterion. Senator Kefauver displayed a cover showing a woman's severed head and a bloody axe and asked if that was his notion of good taste. Gaines said "yes."

To avoid censorship, the publishers accepted a Comics Code Authority that outlawed a list of such words as "terror" and "zombies," decreed that criminals must always be punished, and tied the hands of the superheroes. The Code hit the industry with a wave of bankruptcies. Gaines lost all his titles except *Mad,* changing the title to *Mad Magazine* to escape the censors.

Wertham later had a change of heart. He denied that he had demanded censorship and claimed that he had found benign aspects in comics fandom. In his last book, *The World of Fanzines,* he admitted that "fanzines are a constructive and healthy exercise of creative drive," but the damage he had done took a long time to repair.

Julie Schwartz played a major role in the recovery. The plots had been simplistic in the early comics, the characters cartoonish. Julie had better taste and inspired better work. I think, too, that the comics, along with film and TV, have changed our culture. Growing up, young readers kept their minds attuned to graphic art and learned to think in pictures as much as words. We've become more visual-minded—bad news for word-minded writers!

This book is evidence of today's fine writing and art. Personally. I owe a huge debt of gratitude to the team of Anderson, Kitson, and Erskine. I'd never expected to be so close to the Justice Society! Kevin Anderson wrote the story, Barry Kitson penciled the drawings, Gary Erskine inked them. Rob Leigh did the lettering. Peter J. Tomasi is the editor. I feel immensely honored by my place in the story.

Finally, in spite of Dr. Wertham, I think the superheroes have been a great force for good. Taking them as role models, young readers have been inspired with high ideals of truth and justice.

COME ON, THUNDERBOLT'S WAITING FOR US.
LORD DYNAMO WAS A MADMAN... BUT HE WAS ALSO A GENIUS.
HURRY, MR. WILLIAMSON!
ALL OF THIS RESEARCH, ALL OF THESE BREAK-THROUGHS. THE... LITERATURE.
WE CAN'T JUST ABANDON EVERYTHING!
AAH!
WHOA!
OH, YOU'RE A BETTER WRITER THAN HE IS ANYWAY, MR. WILLIAMSON.
COME ON, MASTER JOHNNY!
LOOK, THERE'S THUNDERBOLT! FOLLOW ME!

JACK WILLIAMSON'S MEMORIAL SERVICE

Rick Hauptmann

Several hundred people attended a memorial service for Jack Williamson November 16, 2006 in the ballroom of the Campus Union Building at Eastern New Mexico University, Portales, NM. A reception was held in the foyer outside the ballroom following the service.

Several tables had been set up to display various memorabilia from Williamson's life, including his Hugos, Nebulas, and other awards, as well as other items of personal significance he had accumulated over the years.

The program was divided into four parts. Betty Williamson, Jack's niece and the person primarily responsible for his care in recent years, began by reflecting on Williamson's family and community life. She presented family anecdotes and read reminiscences of other friends and family about Williamson and his life. It was apparent that Williamson's status with his family and community was at least equal to that which he had achieved as a science fiction author.

Williamson's long-time friend and colleague, Dr. Patrice Caldwell, made a similar presentation about Williamson's impact during his long teaching tenure at ENMU, and in the academic world in general. She, too, offered commentary from Williamson's colleagues and former students, and it was quite evident that Williamson had not only touched, but significantly influenced, many lives during his teaching career.

Connie Willis reflected on Williamson's many contributions to the science fiction field, including remarks and recollections of her own, as well as appreciations by Walter Jon Williams, Frederik Pohl, Ray Bradbury, Charles Brown, and other members of the SF community. It became abundantly clear to anyone who didn't already know, that Williamson was truly a giant in his field, and that his influence, deeply embedded in the world of SF he had helped to establish, would continue long after his passing.

Following was a video review of Williamson's life, which opened with one of Williamson's favorite songs, "Amazing Grace," played on his favorite instrument, bagpipes. Williamson's life was shown in a series of photographs covering most of his 98½ years, and concluded with excerpts from a PBS documentary from several years ago. The video elicited both laughs and tears from the audience, and was a fine conclusion to a moving tribute to the beloved Grand Master.

Besides Willis, other attendees from the SF community included Walter Jon Williams, Stephen Haffner, Edward Bryant, Laura Mixon, Steven Gould, Jack Speer, and a number of other science fiction fans.

Later, supper was served at Williamson's house for his family and close friends from both within and outside the SF world. Much further reminiscing and discussion of Williamson's life took place, with most people realizing that this would likely be the last such gathering in Williamson's home of the past 60 years. Not a few additional tears were shed.

—Rick Hauptmann

The Mists of Time

MILDRED'S CALL CAUGHT me at breakfast that morning, a burst of light in a dismal day.

"Hack, would you consider joining Thor and me on a desperate adventure?"

The breakfast was a soggy slab of cold cheese pizza and of bitter coffee left over from the night before. The sky outside was brown with New Mexico dust lifted by a gusty wind that rattled the windows of the empty house. I asked what sort of adventure.

"Let Thor tell you," she said. "It's too strange for me."

I'd been in love with Mildred, and her voice brought back a happier past. Before she hung up, I'd promised to drive to her Uncle Ben's ranch, where we'd spent summers together when we were kids.

I'd come to the end of a pitiful season as football coach at Caprock High, nine games lost, though the underweight team had played their hearts out. The principal had warned me my contract would not be renewed. My girlfriend had left me for a Mediterranean cruise with the drama teacher. I felt ready and willing for anything different.

The ranch was two hundred miles away. The girlfriend had taken the car, but I had an old pickup. Driving all afternoon, I found my mind filled with wistful recollections of Mildred and our long summers on the ranch. Older and wiser than I, she'd kept us out of trouble. We rode horses and went swimming, and searched the wind-blown dunes for arrowheads and broken bits of Indian pottery.

Those summers had to end, but later she was my college English teacher. Sitting in her classes, I used to find Milton and Shakespeare swept away by her honey-hued hair and pixie smile. Idle dreams; instructors didn't date students. She'd met Dr. Thor Hanson when he came to lecture on quantum mechanics, and their marriage left me with an ache of loss.

Time and drought had lain heavy on the ranch. The cattle pens were empty, the scanty grass sere and gray. The wheel was gone from the windmill tower we used to climb, the stock tank dry, most of the old cottonwoods leafless and dead. Her uncle had moved into town and I found them there alone.

⋆ ⋆ ⋆

Mildred had heard me coming. Thor came with her out of the old house when I parked. A tall blond Viking, a model of gravitas, he took a moment to recognize me, gave me a craggy smile, and gripped my hand with a warm deliberation. She hugged and kissed me, the way I used to wish she would, and I caught a hint of the lilac scent she'd always worn.

"Dear Hack!" She had a radiant smile. "I'm so glad you can join us!"

Her face looked pinched and pale, and I asked how she was.

"Never better!" Yet I caught an anxious quiver in her voice. "I'll live a thousand years."

"Not quite true." Thor shook his head at her and turned very solemnly to me. "The doctors have found a malignant tumor they won't touch."

"But I won't die!" She tried to smile at me. "Thor has a plan."

"A desperate gamble." He shrugged. "But the only hope I see."

"Tell, Thor!" she begged him. "Tell him what it is."

"That's not easy. Let's not scare him off." He swung to me with a grave, bearlike grace. "Come on in. The project can wait till after dinner. Are you ready for a steak?"

With only a candy bar since that leftover pizza slab, I did. He had the grill heating. Mildred had made a salad. We sat at the old oak table in the kitchen I remembered, and he opened a bottle of wine.

"To Thor and his plan!" She lifted her glass. "It will save my life."

"Perhaps." He shrugged. "If we're lucky."

She took only a sip of her wine. The steak was great, but she had barely touched it. He finished his, reminded her to take her pills, and sat frowning thoughtfully at nothing until she begged him again to tell me about the plan.

"It may turn you off." He gave me a piercing look. "What do you know about quantum mechanics?"

"I heard your lecture on it, back at the university. I don't remember anything."

"No wonder. Quantum science can be hard to take."

"Please, Thor," Mildred begged him. "Make it simple. Just tell him what it does."

"It isn't simple." He scanned my face again. "Einstein refused to believe it. He said God doesn't play dice. It does run counter to common sense. Every particle is also a wave, every wave also a particle. If you know where a particle is, you can't know where it's moving. Einstein himself discovered that what one observer experiences as time, another would see as space.

"Nothing is absolutely certain. Zero isn't always zero. The universe is ruled by the laws of probability. Even the highest vacuum is never really empty. Electrons and positrons hop into it out of nowhere, cancel each other, vanish back into nowhere. But not quite always. Unlikely events do happen. Some fourteen billion years ago, one odd particle failed to disappear. Instead it drained enormous energy out of nowhere and grew until it exploded into the Big Bang that created space and time."

He gave a sharp look.

"Do you get it?"

"Maybe."

Her face drawn with strain, Mildred was fiddling nervously with her glass. I wondered what the Big Bang had to do with her.

"Good!" Thor's voice boomed, his blue eyes blazing. "Fascinating research! I used to imagine the future as a straight line of cause and effect, impossible to change as the past. It isn't. The quantum universe doesn't exist until it freezes out of a chaos of statistical uncertainty. It's like Schrödinger's cat in the box, which is neither dead nor alive until you lift the lid."

He paused to frown at me.

"Thor!" Mildred looked up to scold him. "Don't try to amaze him. Just tell him about the plan."

"Okay, dear." His eyes lingered fondly on her face before he looked back at me. "If you're ready, here it is. I'm working on a new math that gives me a strictly limited control of quantum probability. I can freeze atomic forces, stop all atomic action, though only in very small volume of space. In that narrow space, time is suspended."

"We can skip a thousand years!" she cried brightly. "Till doctors know more and medicine is better. I won't have to die."

"We can try." Frowning, he refilled his glass and mine. "I wrote a paper for *Science.* The peer reviewers turned it down. One of them couldn't get the math. The other faulted my experimental evidence. I've got better results since, but Millie's health was failing before I could publish. We have to be our own guinea pigs."

"A time machine?" I asked.

"No machine. Time flows only one way, as eternal as gravity. We can hope to find a higher civilization and better doctors, but nothing is predictable. We can't be sure of any miracles. And there's no way back." He leaned across the table, eyes narrowed to see my reaction. "If you go, you're gone forever. It's good-by to everything you've ever known."

"If you can." Mildred whispered. "Thor won't go without you."

"Take your time." He raised his hand. "Think it over. We can't do it alone, but I want to be frank about the risks. I can't choose our destination, and Millie isn't very able. It may be madness. We've got nobody else to ask."

"Think about it, Hack!" She wiped at a tear and I heard a tremor in her voice. "Think how much can happen in a thousand years. I dream about the wonders we could find. It ought to be a better world."

I needed only half a minute to think about it. My parents were gone. I'd been the only child. I'd left my closest friends when I took the Caprock job. With no real ties to break, I pushed the glass away and told them I'd had enough of now.

That night I slept in the little room that had been mine on those long-past summers when Mildred and I were children here. Next morning Thor laid out what we would be taking.

"It's hard to guess what we'll need. Today, this is an isolated spot where we shouldn't trouble anybody. A thousand years ahead, and we may fall into the middle of a city. An earthquake. A battlefield. A new ice age."

He had bedrolls, a tiny nylon tent, canned water, a backpack stuffed with food, an aid kit, a tiny pocket telescope, a battery radio. He asked if I could shoot and gave me a police revolver. To answer possible questions about our own time, he had a high school history of the world, maps, a book of photos.

"Maybe too much." He gave me a philosophic shrug. "Maybe nothing we'll need."

His lab was a battered van. He loaded the gear and drove through the brush-grown sand dunes south. We house and stopped on a little grassy flat a thousand miles from nowhere, with only the barren dunes around us. His equipment looked simple: only a square black box he mounted on a tripod. Silver-colored antennas jutted out of it in three directions.

"It's a quantum interference effect," he said. "Opposed forces cancel out. Time is stopped until the effect collapses. To show you how it works, I'll repeat the experiment that was finally successful."

He stepped back, holding the end of a wire attached to the tripod.

"Would you note the time on your watch and lay it on the box?"

My watch read 9:16. I laid it on the box. He stepped farther away and clicked a switch at the end of a wire. I heard no sound, but the top of the tripod was suddenly surrounded with a mirror globe that reflected our distorted images.

"The bubble of suspended time." He nodded at it. "Feel it."

Gingerly, I touched it. It was smooth and slick, neither hot nor cold.

"Push it."

I pushed, gently at first, then with all my strength. It felt solidly unyielding as a brick wall.

"It's set for fifteen minutes." He looked at his own watch. "Nothing enters the pod. Nothing happens in it. Nothing leaves it."

We stood there for a long quarter-hour, his eyes on his own watch, till he nodded.

"Nine-thirty."

I counted seconds. At fifty-nine the globe winked silently away. The tripod looked unchanged. My watch still read 9:16 when I picked it up, but the second hand was jumping normally from mark to mark.

"Okay?" Mildred's anxious eyes were fixed on me. "You'll come?"

My pulse was jumping faster than the second hand, but I caught my breath and said I would.

"Take your last look." Thor waved his arm. "We won't be back."

I glanced around us at the endless waste of low gray dunes and a lone hawk cruising high in a cloudless sky. Thor stacked our gear under the tripod. We stood close around it, and he touched his switch again. My ears clicked. The sun was gone, the sky a sullen overcast.

The sand crumbled under our feet. Mildred swayed unsteadily and Thor caught her in his arms.

"What—" she gasped. "What—"

"We made it!" Thor was elated. "We've jumped a thousand years!"

When I looked down, we were standing on a square platform raised a foot or so above the ground. A high tangle of twisted metal beams fenced us in. Close overhead was a great silver balloon, perhaps twenty feet thick.

"The time pod!" Thor stumbled back, his elation gone to troubled wonder. "It should have collapsed when it dropped us here." He blinked at me. "It can't be real!"

I reached to touch the mirror-bright surface and found it smooth and slick and solid as the bubble around the tripod head had been. Thor stood there a long time, frowning at it, shaking his head. "If it's still here, how did we get out?"

He saw no answer, and I turned to look farther around us. Beyond the piles of old metal, I saw a flat landscape, as arid and gray and desolate, hardly changed in all the centuries since we left it.

"Where are we?" Mildred stared at it. "I thought there would be people. Great cities. Strange machines. I hoped for doctors." She looked uneasily at Thor. "And we can't go back?"

"Don't give up yet." He gave her a hopeful grin. "We knew it was a gamble. Let's wait for the cards to fall. Earth's a big planet, after all, with more to see."

But I saw no roads, no buildings, no sign of any people, no way to get anywhere else. We huddled close together under a great bright balloon. A cold wind gust whipped dust around us.

"Nobody." Thor shook his head, frowning at the ruined ironwork around us. "Nobody's been here," he muttered. "Not lately. Look at the drifted sand."

I saw banks of it piled against the rusted beams.

"Once, I think, we might have met a warmer welcome." He gestured at the ruin. "Maybe with a mob here to greet us. This has the look of a theater. If you can imagine those beams covered with seats—"

He stopped and pointed. "There!"

I found a man walking into the gap that would have been the entrance, a hundred yards away. He froze for a moment when he saw at us, hands raised in surprise, and fell to his knees. His voice lifted in strange, quavery chant.

Thor yelled, "Hello!"

He sprang to his feet, stared back for a moment, and fled in terror. I followed out into the open and saw him running until he was gone beyond the crest of a barren dune.

". . . a possible scenario," Thor was saying, when I got back to him and Mildred. "I left a farewell note at the ranch house. We never got back. People knew what we planned. A thousand years gone by, while—" He shrugged, with a somber face. "While I guess civilization collapsed."

"And no hope left," Mildred whispered. "No hope for anything." She looked crushed, but in a moment she gathered herself to give him a small pale smile. "No matter, dear. You did your best."

"I don't know." He stood there staring into the jungle of broken and eroded metal around us, and shrugged at last, with a bitter little grin. "People must have expected us, but they didn't know when. Fact must have been forgotten, memory turned to myth. They could have hoped for us to bring the history and culture they'd lost. I think they worshipped us. We're standing on an altar."

He nodded at our feet. I saw the bones of some small animal in a little pile of ashes on one corner of the platform, something drying in a clay pot on the other.

"The man we saw could have been a priest, keeping a vigil for our arrival. He could be gone to take the news."

Exploring the site, I found a little adobe hut outside the tangle of ancient metal, empty except for some brown liquid in a pottery jar and a few tattered blankets. I climbed the ruin as high as I could and swept the dusty horizon with the pocket telescope. The semi-desert we left had gone to actual desert. Wind-carved dunes scattered with clumps of cactus stretched out to the far-off shimmer of heat. There was nothing moving except a high-sailing bird, nothing I remembered.

Mildred had no strength for walking far, and we saw nowhere else to go. We waited there all day, with no idea what we might expect. The wind died and the sun blazed hot. We kept into shadow off the motionless balloon and made small meals out of what we had. Night fell. We rolled our beds out on the ancient altar.

Next morning we were still alone. Climbing the old metal again, I found a far-off cloud of yellow dust. It disappeared and rose again above a nearer dune, a little file of horsemen riding under it. I watched until they dismounted a quarter mile away. Some twenty-odd men and women, brown-skinned, no different from those of our own time. A few wore long white robes, the rest beaded or painted buckskin. Some carried bows or lances; I saw no guns.

Smoke rose from a fire. They knelt around it. I heard a rhythmic chant. They rose again and a few came on afoot, three white-robed men ahead. Inside the old arena they stopped near the altar where we waited. Thor called greetings to them in several languages. They knelt, and answered with a chant that must have been a ritual prayer.

They rose when that was over, and three young women came to kneel at the edge of the altar, offering each of us a pottery bowl and a wooden spoon. The bowls held a hot meat stew. Mildred ate little of hers; Thor and I scraped out bowls clean. When we had finished the leader spoke words we didn't understand and finally gestured to let us know they wanted to take us away.

Uneasily, Mildred asked where.

"I've no notion." Thor shrugged. "So long as we're alive, we can hope for the best."

For her, they had a chair that two men carried on long poles. They'd brought horses for Thor and me. We traveled all day. I tried to talk to some of the men, but I heard no words I knew, and they seemed too much in awe to try to learn from us.

Before sunset we stopped at a solitary cluster of trees around a well. The men turned a windlass to pull a big wooden bucket out of the well, with water for the horses and us. A hunter came to join us, with the carcass of a deer on a horse he led. The women grilled the venison and made little corn cakes rather like tortillas.

Next morning we came out of the dunes to flat grassland. A few miles farther, we reached a narrow black pavement that lay straight to the vacant horizon in both directions as far as I could see. We waited there till an odd vehicle cane along it and slid to a silent stop. An open car that had no wheels, it floated a few inches off the pavement. Cheered to see it, Thor grinned and called to Mildred:

"Look at this! High-tech civiliza—"

He stopped to goggle at the passengers climbing out of the car. Totally grotesque, they looked half human, half machine. They walked on two legs each. They had heads and arms. Their eyes were bright enormous lenses, their skins some tight bright gold stuff molded to show the knobs and levers of machine parts under it.

They spoke to us and seemed to listen, but their metallic clicks and drones were gibberish to us, but the men understood. They loaded the tripod and the rest of our possessions on the car, beckoned us into it. Mildred shank away from one that tried to help her.

"They're robots," Thor told her. "Advanced beyond any we ever had. They seem friendly. We may find doctors yet."

"I hope." She tried to smile at me. "Hack, I'm sorry we got you here. I wanted to keep you safe."

The men knelt again and began another chant as the car took us away, gliding east across what once had been the high plains of the Texas Panhandle. Country that had been prosperous farmland, it looked desolate now. All I recalled was gone. Good soil had eroded to deep gullies and bare red clay. The pavement wound through new arroyos, and finally climbed to a flat plateau.

The robots stopped the car in a little cluster of bright silver domes, and barked until we knew we'd reached our destination. Three more came to carry our duffel and take us into a room they had ready for us. Clean but very plain, it held three narrow cots, three chairs, and a table that was bare except for three flat black tablets.

One of them caught my arm and guided me very firmly into a white-walled bathroom. Its yellow metal claws surprisingly nimble, it stripped my clothing off, took me into the shower, washed me very thoroughly with a pine-scented soap, toweled me dry, dressed me in a long white gown.

Mildred and Thor were gone when it took me back to the larger room and seated me at the table. Another golden robot came in with a tray of strange instruments. I could only guess at most of what they were doing, but they took my temperature and blood pressure. They drew blood. They caught my breath in a plastic bag. Their huge lenses peered at tiny images of my internal organs, shaper than X-rays.

Finally they left me alone. Hoping for anything I could understand, I picked up one of the little black tablets. It was something like an e-book, with a row of red buttons along the edge. When I touched one, the tablet chimed softly. I pressed again, and a page of print appeared. Many of the symbols looked like letters of the alphabet, but they made no words I knew.

I tried another button. The tablet chimed a different note and lit with living pictures. I heard human voices, saw human figures, most of them in space suits against strange backgrounds. Black skies flecked with stars. Silver domes on landscapes cratered like the moon. A rocket ship descending to a shapeless asteroid on a cushion of fire.

I was still frowning at the tablet when another robot brought Thor back, dressed as I was in a long white robe.

"Interesting." He shook his head when I showed him the tablet.

"Could be we've found the high-tech world we hoped for. Or is it just a comic book?"

The robots brought Mildred in, robed as we were. She let one of them help her to a chair and turned uneasily to Thor. "What do you think they're doing with us?"

He shrugged. "They don't worship us, but they haven't hurt us either. We'll have to wait and see."

They kept us there in the dome, bringing us small bland meals that often had an odd medicinal taste. We walked the floor for exercise. We tried to question the robots and learned nothing at all. We spent hours over the tablets, but the texts were unreadable, the pictures riddles. They took Mildred away for another examination. She came back weak and pale from something they had done.

"I'd hoped for help." Forlornly, she shook her head. "I don't think they care."

On the eighth day I heard thunder. A robot came to turn the outside wall transparent. Looking out across the flat hilltop, I saw a tall bright metal rocket sinking down on a tail of flame. When the smoke and dust had cleared away, a ramp slid out of it and men in orange jumpsuits came down to meet the waiting robots.

An hour later, one of them was escorted into our room. He had changed from the jumpsuit to a transparent plastic coverall. He wore white gloves and a white mask over his nose and mouth. He stopped at the door, searching us with narrowed eyes. We moved to meet him, but the robots waved us back.

He looked entirely human, in his middle years, with short gray hair and an alert hawk-nosed face. He scanned each of us for a long minute before he turned to the next, speaking to the robots in their brittle dialect. They brought him another flat tablet, one wider than those on the table, and held it to show him a flicker of images somewhat like the anatomical drawings I used to see hanging in doctors' offices.

At last he took the mask off his face, had the robots strip the plastic off a neat white tunic he wore beneath it, and waved them aside. Seeming to relax, he smiled and came on to speak to us.

"Dr. Thor Hansen? Mrs. Mildred Hansen? Mr. Hack Harrison? If I have your names correctly?"

The accent was odd, but now at last I heard words I understood.

"Perfectly." Thor grinned in relief. "We're happy you know who we are."

"Rather narrow quarters for you." He turned to inspect the room. "Have the mechs made you comfortable?"

"Good enough." Thor blinked and shook his head. "If we knew—knew a little more."

"A thousand years!" He chuckled sympathetically. "It's hard to imagine how you feel about it. Your time bubble has been a wonder to us. You should be great informants on the history of your time." He looked inquiringly at Mildred. "Mrs. Hansen, how are you feeling?"

"Better." She gave him an anxious smile. "Since we've met you."

He turned to smile at Thor and offer his hand. "Dr. Hansen, I am Zorath D. A linguist and historian. My fields of study are the Age of Invention and Old English literature. How is my accent?"

"Excellent," Thor said. "And we have questions."

"So do I." He glanced at the bare table. "Do you enjoy alcohol?"

"We used to," Thor grinned. "In moderation."

"So do I. In moderation." I caught a flash of humor in his smile. "Shall we sit?"

He held a chair for Mildred, and we sat at the table.

"You amaze me," Thor was saying. "Your voice and your manner. You might be from our own time."

"Thank you." He shrugged in ironic pleasure. "Libraries survived. Your literature preserved a golden age of civilization. The Victorian novel is my hobby. Charles Dickens, Anthony Trollope, William Makepeace Thackeray."

He clapped his hands. A gold-skinned robot glided in with a bottle of wine and glasses on a tray.

"Our recreation of a Victorian dry sherry." He filled our glasses. "I'd like your judgments."

I'm no judge of wines. Thor called it excellent and asked for a history lesson.

"If you can update us on all the years we've missed."

Zorath sipped his sherry, settled into his chair, and frowned at us as he considered how to start.

"In my own opinion, Queen Victoria presided over the crest of Terran civilization. Your twentieth century saw an explosion of science and technology. Welcome at the time, but disastrous in the long run. Einstein's laws and nuclear engineering. Molecular biology and genetic engineering. Computer science and information engineering. Rocket propulsion and travel in space."

"Disastrous?"

The smile gone, he set his glass aside.

"Unfortunately, progress can limit itself. The new technologies were allowed to run out of control. Medical advances multiplied populations. Teeming billions exhausted resources and poisoned the planet. Forests were cut, soils eroded, oil fields drained. Pollution heated the air, thawed the icecaps, lifted the dying seas. There were floods, famines, wars, pandemics.

"Needless misfortunes. The information engineers might have educated citizens for a united world. The nuclear engineers might have generated limitless power. The genetic engineers might have ended disease and recreated humankind."

With a solemn shrug, he shook his head.

"All such utopian visions were allowed to fail. The nuclear engineer manufactured ballistic missiles. The genetic engineers transformed the Black Flu virus into a weapon for the missiles to carry. The last great war almost depopulated the earth. The sole survivors were isolated groups the virus never reached. Their technologies gone, cultures lost, they reverted to the scattered nomadic tribes you have seen."

He sighed and paused to refill our glasses.

"In space, we've done better. The Black Flu never reached the experimental outposts on the Moon and Mars. Those were never friendly worlds; we live now in free-space habitats, rotating to replicate natural gravity. Cut off from support on Earth, we had difficult centuries, but progress did continue, stimulated but controlled by a severe environment. We've moved beyond you, at least in technology, though I often wish I'd had been born in your Victorian Age."

Listening, Mildred had forgotten her sherry and dropped her glass. It rattled on the floor and a golden mech glided to pick it up. Zorath filled another for her, but she sat motionless, gazing anxiously into his face.

"My wife is not well," Thor said. "Do you think—"

"No matter to us." He shrugged. "You bring us no danger, though medical progress has cost us most of our own natural immunities. Mrs. Hansen's condition did alert the mechs. They examined you all and found no threat to us."

"Her condition? Can it be treated?"

"Very probably." Thoughtfully, he nodded. "If you want to come out to Benching. That's my own habitat, named for a space pioneer."

"If we can," Thor said. "Please!"

"Thank you!" Mildred whispered. "Thank you."

"Mr. Harrison." He turned with a very curious expression. "I wish I could ask you to come with us. You'd have been a most welcome guest, and a valuable informant on the culture of your age."

I blinked at him. "Did the mechs find something wrong with me?"

"Nothing," he said. "They removed any hazardous microorganism you may have carried. You are an excellent specimen of early man."

Bewildered, I could only stare at him.

"What's the problem?" Thor asked. "We couldn't have come here without him."

"A paradox. A paradox of the quantum universe." He shook his head at me. "Something I regret, but we see no way around it."

"What paradox?" Thor asked. "I don't see it."

"The two bubbles of suspended time." He sat there a moment, frowning at me, before he went on. "They've have always been there. Unique in the world. Objects of wonder and sometimes of worship. We had a history for the one that carried you."

He turned to nod at Thor.

"Fragments of your research notes have survived. I've visited the site several times with a team of investigators, observing anything we could and grappling with the riddle of the second bubble. It has no history. Our team leader, Arundec E, has been able to repeat your own time experiments. He is undertaking one of his own. If it verifies his space-time concepts, it may open up the past. I may even be able to visit Victorian England. A possibility I never even dreamed of!"

He turned to look very sharply at me.

"His experiment, Mr. Harrison, is an attempt to send you back to your own time, to the day after you left."

That dazed me.

"Why?" Thor frowned at him. "I don't get it."

"Our observations baffled us until Arundec E found an explanation. He says the future can rule the past. In a symmetric universe, every force should have a counter-force. He thinks he has detected a counter-current in time, flowing from the future into the past and reversing the stream of cause and effect."

He gave me a sympathetic glance, and stopped to refill my glass.

"That's the root of the paradox, Mr. Harrison. He thinks you are caught in an eddy between the streams. Your absence has left a space-time void that is drawing you back to where you were."

I sat there, totally bewildered, stricken voiceless. I'd left nothing I wanted in the past. I didn't want to leave Mildred and Thor. I'd been eager to see Benching and all the wonders of another millennium.

"This guy never asked me." I groped for my wits. "I'm not going back."

"We're sorry." Zorath gave me an apologetic shrug. "Arundec expected you to object, but he says you have no choice."

"How—how can that be?"

"That's the nub of the paradox. Among Dr. Hansen's existing papers there's a copy of a letter from you, assuring Mrs. Hansen's invalid sister that she is safe at last, in the hands of competent physicians who are confident of her recovery. The letter is dated ten days after you left the past."

That was a staggering jolt. I looked at Thor and found him blinking, shaking his head.

"That's it." Zorath turned to Thor. "Arundec says Mr. Harrison must return to write the letter because he has already written it. In other words, his absence caused a fracture in space-time that is healing itself."

I had no choice.

We met Arundec E next morning at a Victorian breakfast of crumpets and kippered herring that Zorath ordered from the mechs. He was an intense dark-skinned man who spoke no Old English and explained nothing to me. When the meal was over, he escorted us out to the field where the spacecraft stood, a splendid silver tower in the morning sunlight.

The mechs carried our luggage up the ramp. Thor shook my hand and stood for half a minute, gripping it silently. Mildred hugged me and tried to stifle a sob. Zorath walked with them up the ramp.

"Wait!" I tried to follow. "I want to go!"

I staggered after them for half a dozen steps. Sudden terror stopped me, a shock of fear I didn't understand. I tried to take another step and couldn't. My feet might have been nailed to the pavement. Paralyzed, chilled with a sweat, I could only stare as they climbed to the air lock and turned to wave a last farewell.

Two mechs and walked me away from the rocket. I turned when they released my arms and stood watching it climb on a thundering tower of cloud. Arundec took me back across the field to an odd little aircraft. Aboard it, he flew us back over the badlands and the desert to those piles of ancient iron that had been a temple.

Motionless as a mountain, that huge bright globe still hung low over a charred ear of corn in the ashes of another fire on the old stone altar. Arundec's time device looked much like Thor's: a little box with three projecting horns. He set it on a tripod close below the globe, had me stand beside it, and stepped away.

I felt a jolt like an electric shock and heard the click of an air pressure change. The sun had jumped far across the sky. That tangle of fallen ironwork was gone. Beyond where they been I saw the low gray dunes I knew. I was back on that flat in Mildred's uncle's ranch, a cold west wind in my face.

Off balance for a moment, I stumbled into a shadow. Looking up, I saw the great silver globe that cast the shadow, another beside it. Two identical pods of suspended time, they shone gold and pink and crimson with the colors of the desert suuset.

Thor's little laboratory van stood where we had left it, the keys still in it, but the sun was down before I found enough of myself to drive back to the ranch house. I found it empty, Thor's farewell letter lying on the kitchen table. Calling Mildred's uncle, I got only his answering machine. I spent the night there alone, with nightmare dreams of ghostly paradoxes come back from the future to haunt me.

Her uncle drove out next morning and called the county sheriff when he heard that Mildred and Thor were gone. A newspaper reporter followed the sheriff. The state police and a camera crew from an Albuquerque station were there before noon, all them hammering me with questions about what had become of Thor and Mildred. They never understood anything I tried to say about the quantum universe, but the great mirror spheres were evidence enough to save me from any legal difficulties.

I live now in the old ranch house. The uncle has fenced the site and paved a road to it through the dunes. I conduct lecture tours to show the twin spheres to tourists who never quite believe I'm inside both of them. It's a job that pays the rent and keeps me occupied.

Sometimes on lonely nights I dream of gold-skinned mechs and silver-bright rocket ships, and try to imagine what life might have been with Mildred and Thor inside those whirling worlds in the sky. I'll never know. No other time pods are known, and I expect no guests from the next millennium.

THE END

"I used to go over to his apartment, and I'd take my terrible stories over. And he'd read them and try to help me become a good writer. And I'm glad that he lived to be almost 100 because his effect on other people, and on me, was titanic—and wonderful."

—*Ray Bradbury*

ABOUT THE CONTRIBUTORS

Kevin J. Anderson is a best-selling author who, with Brian Herbert, is expanding Frank Herbert's *Dune* saga. In 2004, he featured Dr. Williamson in a comic book adventure with the heroes of the *Justice Society of America.*

Greg Bear is the award-winning author of *Darwin's Radio* and *Quantico* as well as the artist for Dr. Williamson's book, *H.G. Wells: Critic of Progress.*

David Brin is the award-winning author of the *Uplift* series and the novels *Earth, Glory Season,* and *Kiln People.*

Charles N. Brown is the founder and editor of *Locus: The Magazine of the Science Fiction Field,* now in its 40th year.

Patrice Caldwell, PhD is a faculty member of Eastern New Mexico University and team-taught science fiction and creative writing with Dr. Williamson for nearly 20 years.

John Clute is a widely published critic and author whose *Encyclopedia of Science Fiction* won the Hugo Award in 1994.

Stephen R. Donaldson is the best-selling author of *The Chronicles of Thomas Covenant, Mordant's Need* and *The Gap Sequence.*

James Frenkel is an editor at Tor Books. He has been the primary editor of the novels of Jack Williamson for over 20 years.

James Gunn is one of the newest Grand Masters as awarded by the Science Fiction Writers of America. His novels include *Kampus, The Listeners,* and a collaboration with Dr. Williamson, *Star Bridge.*

Stephen Haffner is the Big Poobah of Haffner Press of Royal Oak, Michigan, which launched a multi-volume effort in 1999 to collect the short fiction of Dr. Williamson.

Joe Haldeman is the author of the award-winning novels *The Forever War, Forever Peace,* and *Camouflage.* He has been a guest of the Williamson Lectureship on three occasions.

Rick Hauptmann is Dr. Williamson's bibliographer, good friend, and neighbor who co-edited *Seventy-Five: The Diamond Anniversary of a Science Fiction Pioneer—Jack Williamson* in 2004.

Elizabeth Anne Hull is a critic and educator who, with her husband Frederik Pohl, travelled with Dr. Williamson to many international destinations.

Bradford Lyau, PhD taught history at various American and European universities, worked at worked Sandia National Laboratories (Albuquerque, NM), and corresponded academically with Dr. Williamson for thirty years.

Dennis McLellan is a staff writer for the *Los Angeles Times.*

Frederik Pohl is the Hugo & Nebula Award winning author of *Gateway* and *Man Plus* and collaborated with Jack Willliamson on ten novels including the *Starchild* trilogy and *Land's End. Platinum Pohl* is a career retrospective.

Mike Resnick is a multiple Hugo & Nebula Award winning author and editor. In 2005, he edited an expanded edition of Dr. Williamson's autobiography, *Wonder's Child: My Life in Science Fiction* for BenBella Books.

Frank Robinson is the best-selling author of *The Power, Waiting,* and *The Glass Inferno.* His recent books are *Pulp Culture, Science Fiction in the Twentieth Century,* and *The Donor.*

Kristine Kathryn Rusch is an award-winning author and editor. She edited *The Magazine of Fantasy & Science Fiction* and her most recent novel is *Paloma: A Retrieval Artist Novel.*

Robert Silverberg was named a Grand Master in 2004 and has won multiple Hugo and Nebula Awards for his novels and short fiction. Subterranean Press is issuing a multi-volume edition of his Collected Stories.

Michael Swanwick is the author of *Jack Faust, Bones of the Earth,* and his novel *Stations of the Tide* won the Nebula Award in 1991.

Walter Jon Williams is the author of the *Dread Empire's Fall* trilogy, *Hardwired,* and won a Nebula for his 2005 story, "The Green Leopard Plague."

Betty Williamson is Dr. Williamson's niece who lives on the Williamson Ranch with her husband Milz Bickley, their daughter Katie, and her parents, Jim and Nancy Williamson.

Connie Willis is the multiple award-winning author of such novels as *The Doomsday Book, To Say Nothing of the Dog,* and *Passage.* Her next novel is *All Clear.*